CORNISH BRICK MAKING
AND
BRICK BUILDINGS

The exhibit of Cornish Bricks at Wheal Martyn China Clay Museum.

CORNISH BRICK MAKING

AND

BRICK BUILDINGS

John Ferguson
and
Charles Thurlow

First Published 2005
Cornish Hillside Publications
St. Austell, Cornwall PL25 4DW

ISBN 1 900147 40 8 Paperback
ISBN 1 900147 41 6 Hardback

Designed by Fergie
Lelant, Cornwall TR26 3LL

Printed and bound by
Short Run Press
Exeter, Devon EX2 7LW

CONTENTS

COLOURED PLATES

GENERAL

DOMESTIC, COMMERCIAL and INDUSTRIAL BUILDINGS

FOREWORD

The building materials usually associated with Cornwall have been granite and slate. Both have been used for many centuries. Brick making has a long history world wide with an Old Testament reference (Genesis Chapter 11, Verse 3), when the Tower of Babel was being discussed:

'And they said to one another, Go to, let us make brick and burn them thoroughly.'

Brick making in Europe came later led by the Romans who built several brick buildings in Britain during their occupation. Many Roman bricks, characterised by their thinness compared to modern brick, have been reused as for example in St. Alban's Cathedral, Hertfordshire. From Tudor times brick making and the use of bricks gradually spread across Britain initially for use in large houses and furnaces of various kinds. The use of brick in Cornwall appears to date from the 17th century.

In this volume we will attempt to give an introduction to the Cornish Brick making scene from the 17th to the early 20th centuries. This will include details of the equipment used in the brick making process as exemplified by what we know was used in the County, along with a number of contemporary accounts. The County will then be divided into areas and details of the brickworks recorded in these, will be given. In the final chapters we shall consider other fired clay products produced and used in Cornwall as well as mentioning some notable brick buildings both domestic and industrial.

These topics have not been covered in a book previously. The number of brick making sites referred to here will we hope dispel any suggestion that all bricks found in Cornwall are imported. Generally such imports were small in number, although brick and tiles made in the Bridgwater area of Somerset are probably an exception, being brought to Cornwall by sea in ore carrying boats returning empty from Bristol,.

ACKNOWLEDGEMENTS

We have been encouraged by the generosity of farmers, land owners and house-holders who have allowed access to their property and in many cases have spent time helping us with our research. To all of these we extend our grateful thanks together with John Tonkin and Kingsley Rickard for their help during the project and to Colin Bristow who kindly read an early version of the text, making many suggestions for its improvement. Finally, we the authors are responsible for any errors of omission or interpretation which may be in the text.

Throughout the text there are photographs illustrating the brick mark of the majority of the Cornish manufacturers. Some of these are from our own collections, but the majority are from the Wheal Martyn China Clay Museum collection. We are grateful to the Trustees for their kindness in allowing us to photograph much of their collection and use them in this book.

Much information has come from the County Record Office and their listing of brickwork references has been most useful. Other information found in newspapers and maps have been most helpfully provided by the Royal Institution at Cornwall library and the Cornwall Centre and the Calstock Archive. We are obliged to the staff of these organisations.

ABBREVIATIONS

CRO or C.R.O. Cornwall Record Office
O. S. or Ord. Surv. Ordnance Survey
RIC or R.I.C. Royal Institution of Cornwall

End notes for references and sources are given in a numbered sequence at the end of each chapter. The reference numbers in the text itself are enclosed in emboldened square brackets, thus: [ ].

Please note that throughout this book, unless otherwise stated, the maps are not drawn to scale. We have followed the usual convention that north is at the top of the map.

CHAPTER 1

BRICKS IN CORNWALL

In spite of not being noted for the use of brick as a building material or as a brick-making county, Cornwall has at least 70 brick-making sites. Some of these were simple estate brickworks where bricks were burnt on site, to provide bricks for an individual house, associated buildings and, in some cases, walled gardens, while others were commercial scale operations using the latest technology of their day.

The principal building materials of the County are natural stone and it is this that dominates. As the nearest available stone of reasonable quality is generally used, then buildings in areas such as West Cornwall, where granite is the most common, have a markedly different appearance to those of North Cornwall where slate stone is the norm. Thus in spite of the many millions of bricks produced within the County and the large numbers known to have been imported from elsewhere in the United Kingdom, brick structures whether they be domestic or industrial are relatively rare.

These facts are born out by the small number of references to be found in literature devoted to the buildings of Cornwall. For example, in the lists given in Pevsner's Buildings of Cornwall [1], there are just 10 towns or villages listed where brick buildings are referred to. Similarly, in a series of published studies of Truro by a group of local history students, edited by June Palmer, there are only 12 buildings where the use of brick is specifically mentioned. It should be noted that any estimate of numbers of buildings from these and other studies is probably artificially low, as it may not include buildings which are cement rendered disguising the original building material. A short walk through any town or village in the County will show that brick buildings of any kind are comparatively rare.

The use of brick in an industrial situation, although generally restricted to a limited number of specific applications, is probably more common. Indeed the sole reason for many of the brickworks which were established, was to supply the needs of industry.

Throughout the County there are a number of significant brick built town and country houses, although it was not until Victorian times that the material was used to any great extent in domestic and industrial buildings. Even then it was frequently used as a dressing to natural stone for its decorative effect. The other prime domestic use for brick was in the construction of chimneys, often replacing

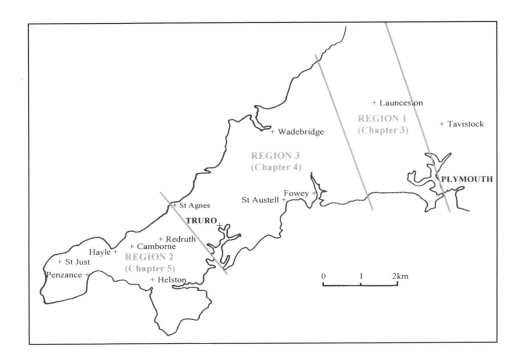

Index map of Cornwall showing the areas into which the County is divided when describing the brick making sites in Chapters 3, 4 and 5.

or supplementing earlier granite structures. Brick and allied products also had many important industrial uses and much of Cornwall's brick and tile production was directed to this end (see table on p.3 for examples). A particularly characteristic use was in the construction of engine house and other chimney-stacks, where brick, being lighter, was the favoured material for the topmost section.

Unlike the rest of England, brick was a relative latecomer to the West Country and in this respect Cornwall was no exception. The reasons for its lack of popularity as a building material are twofold. Firstly, stone for building and slate for roofing were easily and cheaply obtained from local sources and, secondly, it was reckoned that the Cornish weather was inimical to its use. Thus Carew [2], making an early reference to the use of brick in the county comments *"Brick walls can hardly brook the Cornish weather the use thereof being put on trial by some was found so unprofitable as it is not continued by any"*. However in 1758 Borlase (Nat. Hist.) [3] reported: *"There are strata of clay for making bricks in so many places that there is hardly a parish, seldom a large tenement without it, though more generally found in the low and level lands than in the hilly, and not so often near the slaty soil as the loamy"* indicating a change in attitude toward its use.

DATE	LOCATION	STRUCTURE	SOURCE
c.1630	Trelowarren House, Helston	part of house	burnt on estate
c.1670	Trelowarren House, Helston	walled garden	burnt on estate
1634	Tehidy Mansion, Illogan	house (destroyed)	burnt on estate
1679	Stowe House, Kilkhampton	house (demolished)	burnt on estate
1695	Heligan House, Mevagissey	house (now rendered)	burnt on estate
1710	Heligan Garden, Mevagissey	walled garden	burnt on estate
1713	Old Mansion House, Truro	front elevation	upcountry
1710-21	Antony House, Torpoint	house and dovecote	burnt on estate
c.1720	Hatt, Saltash	house	burnt on estate
c.1730	Princes House, Truro	front elevation	upcountry?
1770	Knill's House, St. Ives	upper storey	Dutch brick
1753	Lawrence House, Launceston	house	upcountry?
1780	Branwell's House, Penzance	house	Dutch brick
c.1820	Heligan Garden, Mevagissey	walled gardens	burnt on estate
c.1820	Trengwainton Garden	walled garden	Dutch brick
1856	Levant Mine, St. Just	man-engine stack	locally made
1870	Levant Mine, St. Just	Brunton calciner	Marazion
1870	Trounson Building, Redruth	shop (polychrome)	St. Day
1871	Giew Mine, St. Ives	engine ho. dressings	St. Day
1875	Alms Houses, Padstow	houses	Somerset?
1878	Tregonning Hill, Breage	brick kiln lining	Lee Moor
1880	Swing Bridge, Hayle	engine house	Bridgwater
1889	Gasworks, Hayle	dressings	Bridgwater
1890	National Explosives, Hayle	Acid Battery	Grampound Road
1890	National Explosives, Hayle	Acid Battery, floor	North Wales
1890	National Explosives, Hayle	Acid Battery, flues	Garnkirk
1890	National Explosives, Hayle	Acid Battery, stack	G.W.R., Swindon
c.1890	Porthmeor, Zennor	arsenic calciner, bed	Cowen, Blaydon
1897	Poldice Arsenic Works	calciner & labyrinth	St. Day
1898	Coodes Bank, St. Austell	commercial	Carloggas & Ruabon
1900	Levant Mine, St. Just	Brunton calciner, lining	St. Day
1920	Leswidden Clay Dry	fireboxes & flues	Wheal Remfry

Some dated Cornish brick buildings and structures showing the range of building types and sources of most of the bricks used.

In their well respected study of Cornish domestic architecture, Chesher and Chesher [4] comment in a discussion on patterns of 18th century house building: "*brick was avoided by Cornish builders, until this period*". After listing some 18th century examples, they make the observation that in each case cited, brick was subsidiary to stone. They further make the observation that "*In small houses it* [brick] *did not make much headway except for chimneys, where it became very common, ——*". Observation suggests that the use of bricks in the construction of chimneys was also common in the 19th and early 20th centuries, and can be considered part of the vernacular architecture of the County. Of the notable Cornish brick buildings Ince Castle, near Saltash is usually quoted as the earliest, being built c.1630 with brick imported from the Continent (Alec Clifton-Taylor [5]. Another early building which is partly constructed of local brick is the Old Pennance Farm, Grampound, which is probably of a similar date. Although the old town of Penzance was rebuilt after it was sacked by the Spaniards in 1595, it is not until the 18th century that brick was used for building. Peter Laws [6] records that some brick and granite buildings, built from 1775 onward, survive in Chapel and Parade Streets.

There are a number of references to houses which were built from brick made on site and we can mention three of the better known examples. Firstly Heligan House in St. Ewe parish, where surviving building accounts dated 1695 – 1740, record that during the building campaign, the bricks used to construct the house were burnt on site, utilizing clay dug on the estate. Another example is Trewithen built c.1715, where the front elevation was brick with granite dressings. Sadly it has now been cement rendered, because the brickwork had become porous over time. Two detached wings of the house, constructed from pink brick, survive as built. The third example is Antony House near Torpoint, built 1710 – 1721, where part of one wing of the house is brick built and some of these bricks can be seen to show an indentation, a sign that they were fired too soon after they had been moulded. The nearby estate dovecote which is thought to be coeval with the house, is also constructed from brick.

In Truro and Launceston, there are a few early brick built houses of note. Those in Truro include The Old Mansion House c.1713, and Princes House c.1730, while in Launceston Castle Hill House and Lawrence House were both probably built c.1753, as well as several others of similar age. These may all have been built from brick imported from elsewhere in England or even Europe.

1.1 HISTORY OF BRICK MANUFACTURE IN CORNWALL

In spite of the fact that bricks imported from upcountry manufacturers were often cheaper than the local product, the Cornish industry developed apace during the 19th century, with its heyday between 1870 and 1880. Decline, due to outside factors started in 1890. Among these were the general economic situation; the high price of the coal needed for firing and the commencement of concrete block manufacture from waste sand from china clay workings and mine dumps using Portland cement. The brick-making industry did however continue, albeit on a much reduced scale, during the 20th century. The last of the building brick manufacturers closed during the 1960's, to be followed in 1972 by a brickworks, which had been supplying specialist firebrick for the heated floors of drying kilns used in the china clay industry for about 100 years.

Bricks are made by firing a mixture of clay and filler, usually sand, which has been moulded into a block of suitable shape and size, at a high temperature. Bricks made and fired in this way should not be confused with concrete blocks, sometimes referred to as 'bricks' in Cornwall. Elsewhere in England fillers such as ashes were a favoured alternative. For example London stock bricks, so beloved in the Home Counties, were made using a mixture of ashes and chalk as filler. This gave London stocks their characteristic texture and yellow colour. In Cornwall a variety of raw materials have been used to make brick and the following list is roughly in order of their historical use:

Head - the local name for a mixture of weathered rock and wind borne dust called 'loess', formed during the Ice Ages. This can be a stoney or a clayey silt – for example Hannafore Brickworks, Looe.

China Clay By products - residues from the sand drags and mica refining channels containing fine sand, coarse clay and mica - for example Carloggas.

Decomposed Granite - used because the clay was too iron rich for china clay – for example Carbis. The iron had some value as a flux in brick making.

Decomposed elvan - a fine grained granitic rock, which has been decomposed by weathering – for example most of the Tamar Valley works.

River/estuarine mud – for example Tolcarne Brickworks, Newquay. Also sources from rivers draining the china clay areas which carried china clay residues - as at Par.

Shale   a fine grained sedimentary rock whose principal component is clay. Often decomposed, particularly in near surface outcrop – for example Millbrook. Slate is its metamorphic equivalent, Also used for example in the Millbrook area.

The methods used to get the raw materials include digging, quarrying or even mining. This was followed by the earliest stage of preparation, which could include all or some of the following: weathering, crushing and mixing. In the mixing process a sandy filler can be incorporated and mixing was carried out either by hand or by passing through a pug mill (see later) where it was literally minced to produce an even, lump free consistency. In earlier times clay was dug in the autumn and left exposed to the weather over winter. The rain and frost would break the clay down making it easier to work, so that the process of making bricks then was a spring or early summer occupation.

Decomposed Elvan	Head	River/Estuary Mud	Shale	Decomposed Granite
Calstock F B Co.	Grampound Road	Acme, Marazion	Devoran	Burthy
Gunnislake	Hannafore	Charlestown Pond	Foss	Carbis
Phoenix	Lizard	Devoran	Millbrook	Carkeet
Porth	Portmellon	Kiggon	South Down	Carloggas
Quintrell Downs	Charlestown, Brick Hill	Lamoran	Whitstone	St. Day
Tamar	Red Post	Mylor		Tregonning Hill
Trevarth.	St. Ewe	Newham, Truro		Wheal Grey
Wheal Remfry	Sticker	Par		Wheal Remfry
Gaverigan	Swanpool/Pennance	Tolcarne		
		Trelonk		

Some *sources of raw material used in some Cornish Brick Works. The group labelled 'shale' also includes works where fine grained sedimentary rock was used.*

Following the mixing and homogenization of the raw materials, individual bricks were moulded, either by hand or machine to a standard size which takes into account shrinkage when the brick is fired. In general it can be said that in the British Isles, bricks have increased in size since the Middle Ages. In particular, the Brick Tax of 1784 led to manufacturers making larger bricks, in order to dodge the full tax (the Brick Tax was repealed in 1850). Before metrication the standard brick size was: 9 inches (229 mm.) length 4 ½ inch (114 mm.) width and 2 ¾ inch (70 mm.) thick. Measurements of locally made bricks throughout the County shows that the length ranges between 8 ¾ inches (222 mm.) and 9 inches (229 mm.), while the width is between 4 ¼ inches (108 mm) and 4 ½ inches (114 mm.). The thickness ranges between 2 5/8 inches (67 mm) to 2 ¾ inches (70 mm.). An exception are bricks thought to have been made by the Lizard Brick and Tile Company whose length was 8 ½ inches (216 mm.) with a width of 3 ¾ inches (95 mm.) [7].

The moulded bricks were then air dried, so that most of the water in the clay could evaporate, leaving the bricks 'leather-hard'. Until the 19th century this drying process was carried out under a simple structure with open sides for good air circulation, commonly referred to as a 'hack'. When the bricks had reached the correct state of hardness, they were fired either in a clamp or kiln. More details will be found in Chapter 2. In order to produce good building brick a temperature of around 1000° C had to be reached and for this purpose coal, in general use after c.1750, was probably the best fuel. For the manufacture of firebricks an even higher temperature of around 1150° C was required. As we have already commented some of the Counties late 17th - early 18th century houses were built from brick which would have been burnt in clamps, using furze, which burns at a very high temperature. Dried furze or gorse, which was a common fuel for both domestic and industrial uses, was collected in the autumn and left to dry-out in covered stacks over the winter.

Although the firing temperature and position in the kiln are two factors governing the colour of the burnt brick, the composition of the clay is more significant and is largely dependent on the amount of iron oxide in the raw material. Thus for example the Cornish raw materials such as decomposed elvan and shale rocks which contain significant quantities of iron oxide give rise to bricks which are various shades of red. On the other hand, the more common Cornish-made bricks were made from china clay residues which contain little iron, are light in colour often being creamy-white.

1.2 USE OF BRICK

As well as its use in mass walling, brick was also used extensively as a decorative dressing on stone (and in the case of Cornwall, mainly granite) buildings, where it can appear in the quoins, around doorways and windows, as well as lining arches. In this context it can be seen in both domestic and industrial building. Another important use, already mentioned, is in the construction of domestic chimney-stacks. An application originally unique to Cornwall is its use for the construction of the top sections of Cornish Engine House chimney-stacks [8].

*Part of the south west elevation of the old gasworks, East Quay, Hayle.
Built 1889. Showing the use of dressed granite with red brick dressing.*

The use of brick in domestic and industrial chimney stack construction.
Top Left: *Combined 18th Century granite stack with 19th Century brick stack, Lelant.*
Top Right: *Power House and chimney stack, Levant Mine.*
Bottom left: *Smithy chimney, Coverack. Note that these bricks are thinner than normal which suggests that they are imported Dutch brick.*

In smaller domestic properties bricks were also used for floors, being a cheap replacement for traditional slate slabs or lime ashes. Sadly as bricks are porous these floors are usually damp so that most have been replaced or covered. The surface of ore or coal storage plots were also occasionally paved with brick, such as the coal store on North Quay, Hayle. Although in Cornwall granite is usually used in the construction of the supporting pillars of railway viaducts and the abutments of bridges, there are a number of exceptions, for example the Hayle Viaduct where dense blue brick is used.

Wall of outbuilding, near Brick Hill, Charlestown.

Ropewalk Pilchard Cellar, St. Ives. Now demolished.

Brick base of buddle, Botallack Mine.

Wall of Alms Houses, Middle Street, Padstow.

Garden Walls: Heligan Garden.

Garden Wall, Trengwainton Garden.

Garden Walls: Trelowarren House

Supporting Pier, Hayle Viaduct.

Brick colour: Red Shades (locations noted)

Fore Street, Marazion.

Tram House, West End, Redruth.

Harris Memorial Hall, Illogan.

Bird in the Hand (Public House), Hayle.

Cleaning area of Victorian Dairy, St. Michael's Mount.

Found during excavation at Levant Engine House.

Wheal Martyn China Clay Museum

St. Ives Museum

Brick colour: Cream shades (locations noted)

Chimney stack, Carkeet Brickworks.

Grove Place, Falmouth.

North Street, Marazion.

Mine Chimney stack, Wheal Metal, near Sithney.

Plug door, Giew Mine engine house. near St. Ives.

Brick colour: Polychrome brickwork (locations noted)

Examples of brick bonds commonly used by Cornish builders.
Top: *English garden-wall bond, Trelowarren House garden wall. C*entre Left: *English bond, Padstow.* Centre Right: *Flemish bond, Bird in the Hand, Hayle.* Bottom Left: *Stretcher bond, Truro.* Bottom Right: *Dutch bond, Hayle.*

The strength and stability of brick walls result from the type of bond used during construction. There are a number of commonly used bonds including Stretcher, English bond, English cross bond, English garden wall bond, Dutch and Flemish bonds and some examples are shown opposite. The bond can also be exploited to give a pleasing decorative effect. And, as we shall see later, houses built during the late Victorian or Edwardian periods are often characterised by decorative brickwork, with patterns created using flared headers [9] or by using contrasting coloured brick to create polychrome patterns. Other attractive effects can be created using brick dressings which can be either polychrome or monochrome with natural stone. In a small number of examples in the county, glazed brick has been used both internally and externally. Bricks are also made in a variety of different shapes, known as specials, some of which are made particularly for decoration. Among the more common types are bull nose bricks, plinth bricks and voussoirs [10].

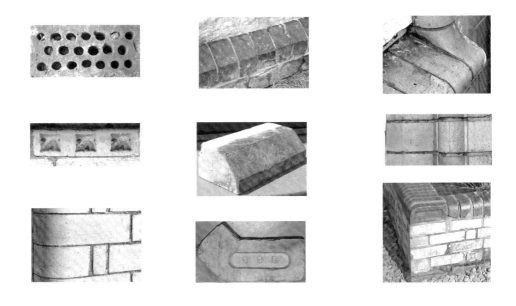

Brick Specials.
Top Row (Left to Right): *Perforated red brick - ubiquitous in Cornwall. Plinth header in dark plumb coloured brick, Hayle Gasworks. "Cow nose" plinth header and return, Tram House, West End, Redruth.* Middle Row (Left to Right): *"Dog Tooth" moulded brick, Harris Memorial Hall, Illogan. Plinth stretcher, Hayle Power Station. Concave moulded header, Tram House, West End, Redruth.* Bottom Row (Left to Right): *Bull Nose, Tram House, West End, Redruth. Dog Leg brick from Milbrook, exhibited at Wheal Martyn China Clay Museum. Bullnose blue brick above white glazed brick, Venning's Fountain, Callington.*
Note: *Not all of the bricks illustrated were made in Cornwall. for example the perforated brick was probably made at Bridgwater in Somerset, while those from Tram House, and the Harris Memorial Hall were probably made at Newton Abbot, Devon.*

1.3 IDENTIFICATION OF BRICK MANUFACTURERS

Generally brick makers mark their bricks with some form of identification, by impressing their mark into the partially dried brick before firing. These brick marks were introduced to allow the ready identification of the products of individual brickworks, preventing fraudulent selling of inferior bricks masquerading as those from a reputable works. Most early bricks, particularly those fired for a particular building were very rarely marked and in these cases it is only when original documentation has survived, that we can be sure of identifying the manufacturer.

The brickmark can be the name of the site of the brickworks, for example CARLOGGAS; or its owner, such as W.A, the brick mark of William Argal who operated Wheal Grey brickworks near Penzance; or the name of the nearest large town thus LISKEARD was used by the Carkeet brickworks. Other brickmarks such as VULCAN, a mark of the Pennance works, near Redruth, were used to promote sales by suggesting that the brick has exceptional qualities.

Colour as we have seen is dependent on two main factors, these being the chemical composition of the raw materials and, in particular, the amount of iron oxide present as well as the firing temperature. Temperature is in part controlled by the position of the bricks in the kiln during firing. A further contributor is the atmosphere in the kiln during firing which can control which particular oxide of iron is formed and hence the colour of the finished product. For example an oxidising environment inside the kiln will produce bricks of a red colour, while a reducing environment (lack of oxygen) will produce very dark, blue coloured bricks.

Bearing these factors in mind it is clear that colour can only be used in identification of manufacturer with extreme caution. In Cornwall we can say that pale coloured creamy white bricks were made at brickyards where waste from china clay working, or decomposed elvan was readily available, while red bricks were made from either head, sedimentary rocks or more rarely river estuary mud. There are exceptions to this and at least one brick maker appears to have used clay from more than one source.

To summarise we can only be sure of an identification of bricks in a particular structure if we can see a brick mark or there is documentary evidence indicating the source of the bricks.

It is self evident that brick marks can only be seen on bricks from structures which are ruinous or are being demolished. In the case of industrial buildings dating from the 19th century, we can often see marks, because of their state of disrepair. With domestic property on the other hand, we are generally not so lucky and are largely reliant on documentary evidence or, occasional, circumstantial evidence such as a local brick works producing brick at the time of the building of the property.

1.4 IMPORTED BRICK

It is known that during the 17th and 18th centuries, brick was brought to England from the Low Countries, particularly in ships returning in ballast. It has been suggested that this also applied in Cornwall, although there is little documentary evidence of this. One criteria used to identify such bricks is their thickness which is normally less than the traditional English brick.

One example of a building for which this source has been suggested is Knill's House [11] situated in Fore Street, St. Ives and built in the third quarter of the 18th century. Sadly there is little hard evidence that this was so and, although it has not proved possible to measure the bricks they appear to be of normal thickness. Again in Chapel Street, Penzance the terrace comprising numbers 25, 26 and 27, originally known as Rotterdam Buildings are said to have been built in 1784 using bricks taken from a Dutch ship bound for America [12]. These particular bricks have been measured and do not differ significantly from the normal British standard size.

Number 25, Chapel Street, Penzance. The house where Maria
Branwell, mother of the Bronte sisters was born in April 1793.

The smithy chimney on the end of Jiggers Cellar, Coverack on the other hand (page 8), is built from thin bricks. These bricks could be of could be of Dutch origin and Cyril Hart [13] has suggested that the chimney was built by a Dutch mason.

Local records suggest that large quantities of brick were imported from upcountry manufacturers both before and after the County was connected to the rest of England by the railway. For example in Truro, The Old Mansion House, built during the first decade of the 18th century, is recorded as having been built with brick imported from London [14]. The Bassett home, Tehidy Mansion, near Illogan, also incorporated brick brought from London which were landed at the port of Hayle in 1735 [15]. As we shall see later brick for use in the building of the house was also burnt on site.

There is published documentary evidence that the ships carrying copper ore to the smelters of South Wales from West Cornwall, would often return empty and call at Bridgwater to collect a cargo of brick and, on occasions, roofing and ridge tiles. One of the principal ports involved in the import of bricks and other burnt clay products in West Cornwall was Hayle and in the 18th and 19th century there were at least two firms involved. The companies were the Cornish Copper Company (C.C.C.), later Sandys, Carne & Vivians' Copperhouse Foundry in the Copperhouse area of the town and Harvey & Co. who operated Hayle Foundry at Carnsew, usually referred to as Foundry. These two firms operated in direct competition with each other and with some animosity, particularly in the early days.

Published records show that in 1758 the C.C.C. held large stocks of brick, while a stock evaluation in 1883 just before the Company went into liquidation, again indicated large stocks of brick and roofing tiles [16]. There is good evidence to suggest that these items were imported rather than home produced. Elsewhere, in a letter book covering the period August 1791 to February 1796, we are told that Harvey & Co. were importing bricks and tiles from Bridgwater and Hawarden in Flintshire. There is also a record of a letter dated 9th January 1795 addressed to the captain of one of Harvey's ships, to shop around in Bridgwater, to get the best deal for purchasing bricks and ridge tiles [17].

The industrial buildings of the County have yielded large numbers of imported firebricks, not only from Devon (Candy and Hexter, Humpherson), but from such diverse areas as Tyneside (Ramsay and Cowen) and Glasgow (Garnkirk). Another source of bricks was the Channel Islands (Copp of Jersey). One brick whose source is not known is buff coloured, with no frog and marked "CORY". A few have been found in West Cornwall and this could be a local, as yet unrecorded brickworks, or more likely, an import.

As with many other building materials, bricks were frequently sold second hand when buildings were demolished. A good example of this practice is found at the Porthia China Clay Works (near St. Ives), which was built in the early 1920's using second hand bricks bought from the then recently demolished National Explosive Cos. works at Upton Towans, Hayle. This is a particularly clear example as there are large numbers of marked acid-proof bricks at Porthia, matching those still to be found in what remains of the National Explosives Company nitric acid battery at Upton Towans. Also at Porthia, the flue carrying the gases from the clay dry to the chimney, is lined with bricks made by the Garnkirk Company of Glasgow, which ceased production during the first decade of the 20th century. Again there are matching bricks to be found in some surviving flues at Upton Towans.

A further site where second hand bricks must have been used is at Taylor's Shaft at Pool near Redruth. Here the flues and chimney stack and the remains of the boiler house all built in the 1920's, contain many bricks and other burnt clay products from brickworks such as St. Day, which had long ceased production. Part of the flues themselves have been recently rebuilt to enable tourists to walk from the exhibition centre on the site to the engine house and various brickmarks can now be seen in the floor of the flue, especially near the exit, where part of the original flue has survived.

Although the manufacture of bricks in Cornwall has now ceased, there is a process in the china clay industry which requires bricks of china clay to be made as a first stage of the process. This is in the manufacture of calcined clay for refractory products, where briquettes of clay are burnt in a tunnel kiln at high temperature. The bricks are then crushed and the product graded and sold under the trade name 'Molochite' [18].

The picture shows a truck of china clay briquettes coming out of a gas heated tunnel kiln, after firing at up to 1500°C.

END NOTES

1 Pevsner N. revised Radcliffe E. 1970 "The buildings of England Cornwall"
   Penguin Books, Harmondsworth, Mddx., England

2 Carew, 1602, Survey of Cornwall

3 Borlase Nat. Hist., 1758, p.63

4 Chesher V. M. and Chesher F. J. 1968 "The Cornishman's House" D. Bradford
   Barton Ltd., Truro, England. p.102

5 Alec Clifton-Taylor in Pevsner & Radcliffe 1970, "The Buildings of England
   – Cornwall", Penguin Books, Harmondsworth, Middlesex. p.30

6 P. Laws in Pool, P. A. S. 1974 "The History of Penzance" The Corporation of
   Penzance, Cornwall. p.184

7 There may be some oversize bricks in the earliest surviving part of Harvey's Hayle
   Foundry, constructed c1790.

8 As the use of Cornish Engines spread to mining districts world wide, so did the use
   of brick top sections of their chimneys.

9 Flared bricks are those which have been accidentally or deliberately burnt at such
   a high temperature, that the clay has vitrified on the surface of the brick. This can
   happen when one face (frequently the end or header face) has been exposed to
   flames in the kiln.

10 Voussoir - a wedge shaped brick used when building an arch

11 John Knill who was a Customs Officer in St. Ives lived here in the third quarter of
   the 18th Century.

12 Hill & Kerrow 1996 "The Penzance Home of Maria Branwell", p.1

13 Cyril Hart, 1990 "Cornish Oasis - a Biographical Chronicle of the Fishing Village
   of Coverack, Cornwall" The Lizard Press, Mullion, Cornwall. p.47

14 Truro Buildings Research Group 1976 "Truro Princes Street and the Quay Area"
   p.9

15 Tangye, M. 2002 "Tehidy and the Bassets" p.12

16 Pascoe, W.H. 1981 "The History of the Cornish Copper Company" Dyllansow
   Truran, Redruth, Cornwall

17 Vale E. 1966 "The Harvey's of Hayle" p.232-234

18 Thurlow, C. 2005 "China Clay from Cornwall and Devon - The Modern China
   Clay Industry" 4th. Revised Edition, pp.53-54.

CHAPTER 2
BRICK MAKING METHODS IN CORNWALL

2.1 19th CENTURY BRICK MAKING EQUIPMENT

Although the equipment used at individual Cornish brickworks, either recorded or observed, will be mentioned in the site accounts later, it is appropriate at this stage to illustrate and discuss in general terms the equipment widely used by brick makers. Many of the items will be related specifically to brick manufacture in Cornwall later in the chapter.

The first part of the process of brick making involves grinding and mixing the clay. The most commonly used piece of equipment is the pug mill, which was a cylindrical machine that mixed and blended the clay and any additives by the action of rotating knives or blades. It was designed to produce a homogeneous material of the correct consistency to be used directly by the brick maker. Since it was difficult to remove all but the largest pieces of solid material before pugging, a second method was to grind the coarser material by the use of rotating rollers. These could be similar to the crusher rolls developed in Cornwall and used in the mining industry, where the material to be ground passed between two counter rotating rollers which were kept in close contact. Another favoured method was the grinding pan or edge runner mill, in which two large and heavy cast iron wheels, rotate to crush the raw material against the bottom of the pan. In pre-19th century brick works, pugging was frequently carried out by the simple expedient of men or animals (usually oxen), paddling in the clay until it acquired the correct consistency to enable the bricks to be moulded easily. Men working bare footed had an advantage, as they could find any large pieces of stone and reject them! Although not recorded, it is fairly certain that this was the method used on the Cornish estate brickworks.

Three power sources could be used to drive the pugging and grinding and other equipment, they were horse-power, water-power or steam. In the first, the vertical pug, a horse walking in a circular path around the equipment turned an overhead beam which was connected to a central spindle carrying the knives to cut and knead the clay or rotate the rollers in the edge runner mill.

When a water-wheel or steam engine was the source of power, it was connected to the pug mill or crushing equipment either by gearing or by a pulley belt. For

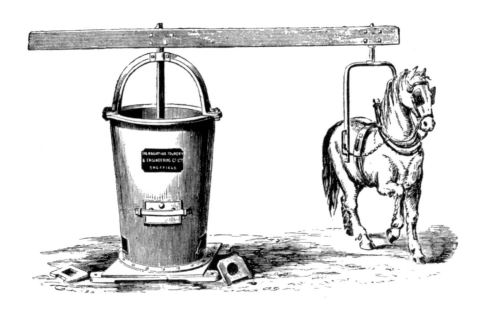

An early horse-driven vertical pug mill from Bourry. "A Treatise on the Ceramic Industries". 1926Ed., p.279, Fig. 176

Horizontal pug mill from Bourry, 1926Ed., p.95, Fig. 28

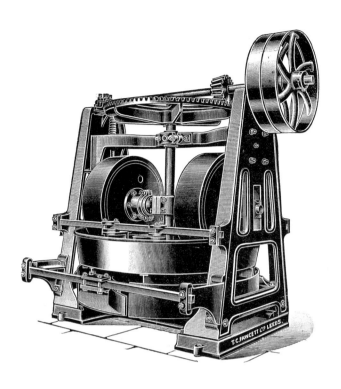

Edge runner mill from Bourry, 1926Ed., p.74, Fig.13

Crushing rolls and pug mill. From Bourry, 1926Ed., p.99, Fig. 33

example the horizontal pug mill illustrated (page 20) has a belt drive and a gear train which could be connected to a water-wheel or steam engine. The gear train ensured that the knives rotated at the correct speed.

Earlier crushing pans, like pug mills, were horse driven, the horse being tethered to one end of a pole or beam which was connected, at the other end, to a vertical spindle which carried a horizontal axle with rollers at either end. Of the various later forms of crusher developed, two belt driven machines are illustrated. The first of these, an edge runner mill (page 21), has a crushing pan with a pair of heavy rollers which rotated in the pan, grinding and crushing the material it contained. The resulting clay mix was extruded through perforations in the bottom of the pan. The second, is a combined rolls and pug mill. In this machine the clay mixture would have been fed into the top of the roll crusher from whence it passed immediately into the pug mill. Clearly both of these devices were designed to be driven either by water or steam power.

When the clay and any additives had been mixed to the right consistency, it would then pass to the next stage of the process where it would be moulded to form a brick. This process although traditionally carried out by hand was also mechanized to increase productivity to meet the demands of the expanding building industry. However the skill of brick making by hand has not died out and even today bricks manufactured this way command a better price than the machine-made equivalents. Hand moulded bricks are made in an open mould box such as shown below. The process is simple, the brick maker fills the mould with clay compressing it on the bench, to ensure that all the corners are filled and to create a flat underside. Any surplus clay is then struck off the top to give a flat surface. The brick is then released from the mould and placed somewhere convenient to become partially dry. A stock board, which is a brick sized board attached to the bench so that the mould can be placed over it, can also be used. The stock board can be flat or it can have a raised central portion or kick (see Penzance brick making account), which will create a hollow or frog in the brick. The stock board could also carry raised letters which would have impressed the makers mark onto the brick. Frogs come in various forms and may or may not incorporate a maker's mark. A number of brickmarks on bricks collected from various Cornish sites are shown opposite. The brick illustrated bottom left has a frog.

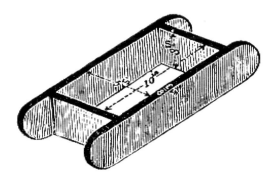

Wooden brick mould from Searle, 1956Ed., p. 128, Fig.43. (The dimensions given on the drawing are 10 x 5 x 3 inches - this size allows for shrinkage during firing.)

Some examples of Brickmarks of manufacturers from outside Cornwall.
Top Row: *Tyneside brickworks* (Ramsay & Cowen).
Middle Left: *Devon* (Candy).
Middle Right: *Channel Islands* (Copp).
Bottom Left: *Somerset* (W. Thomas & Co., Wellington).
Bottom Right: *Glasgow* (Garnkirk).

A later development was the use of hand presses operated by either levers or by a screw mechanism. The press was used to produce a better quality brick, which would be denser and free from air bubbles or other defects which could cause problems during firing. Most facing bricks would be pressed. Such presses were often used to press the partly dried bricks. If a makers mark was required, stamp plates with the brickmark would be used in conjunction with the press. For this the operator had to be very careful, keeping the stamp plates clean so as to give a clear impression of the mark on the surface of the brick.

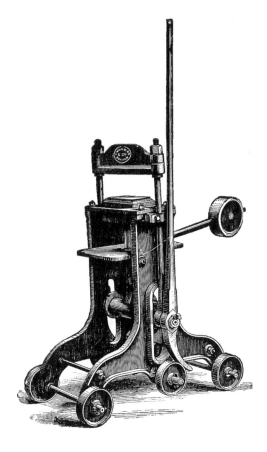

Adjustable lever operated mechanical brick press from Searle. "Modern Brickmaking", 1956 Revised Edition, p.141, Fig. 53.
This is very similar to the press known to have been used at Trelonk brickworks.

A development on the road toward full mechanization of the brick making process, was to extrude the compacted clay from the pug mill through a die to give a continuous block of clay which when cut to an appropriate size, would produce a number of bricks. Such a machine is shown opposite (top), where an extruded block of clay can be seen to have been cut by a line of taught vertical wires, to give several bricks. The cutting bench itself, which could be separate from the machine which extruded the clay block, is shown in more detail opposite (middle). Although the associated equipment is driven by mechanical means the wire cutting process illustrated is operated manually.

The early brick making processes just discussed have left their mark on the bricks produced by them, some of which can be recognized in buildings and other structures, giving a clue to the production methods used. The photograph opposite (bottom), illustrates bricks with striations on the bed face, which is a frequent characteristic of bricks which were wire cut. Another example (page 26, top), shows that the mix used to produce the bricks was not homogeneous and large pieces of coarse material can be clearly seen. This indicates poor grinding and pugging. Also in this photograph note the poor state of the brick work which is due partly to attack and partly due to the exposed situation, on a cliff top facing the Atlantic Ocean.

Top: *Early combined brick machine from Searle, 1911Ed., p.78, Fig. 38.*
Bottom: *Cutting table from Bourry, 1926Ed. p.125, Fig. 73.*

Bricks showing striations, evidence of the use of wire cutting during manufacture. Lining of bottom of buddle, Botallack Mine.

Brick made using badly ground and mixed raw material. Exposed due to a combination of acid attack and weather. Copper extraction tanks, Levant Mine.

2.2 DRYING AND BURNING

After hand moulding, green bricks contain too much moisture to be fired immediately and therefore need some preliminary drying. Originally such drying was carried on out of doors, the newly made bricks being stacked so that air could circulate freely around them to allow the moisture to evaporate. Some form of protection such as thatch or a tarpaulin would be put over the stack to keep off the rain. They would then be left until they had lost much of their moisture and had become what is commonly described as "leather-hard".

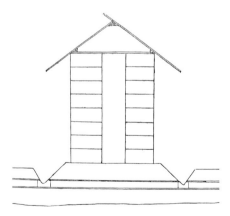

The hack, an early form of dryer used to partially dry the bricks before firing. From Searle, 1956Ed., p. 138, Fig. 50

From this simple method of drying the hack was developed which allowed drying to take place under permanent cover. The hack which in some respects was similar to the system used in the early days of the china clay industry, was simply a roof on stilts covering rows of shelves upon which the bricks could be stacked with sufficient space between them, to allow good air circulation. The jacket of this book shows hacks at Par brickworks. Which ever of these two methods was employed, the drying process could be quite protracted particularly during cold wet spells, taking between 3 and 6 weeks or even longer. This factor led to the development and use of a dry which was heated, usually underfloor as in the Cornish clay-dry. During the late 19th century, heated tunnels began to be used for drying and firing. Some remains of a very early example can be seen at Shaugh Bridge in Devon [1]. A further advance which helped speed up or eliminate the drying process, was the development of brick making machinery which could mould and press much drier clay than that used traditionally by the brick maker.

When the bricks were judged to be sufficiently dry so that they would retain their integrity when fired, they were transferred to a kiln or clamp for burning. The oldest method which is still used occasionally, was the clamp. This was a temporary structure, formed from the bricks to be burnt and the fuel required to perform the burning. The clamp, which could be set up in a brickyard or on a building site where the bricks were to be used, consisted of alternate layers of fuel and green bricks, laid on a bed of broken brick (when available) mixed with more fuel. The clamp was lit and left until it had burned through and cooled down, which in the case of a large clamp, could take weeks.

The use of the clamp, although simple and practical, was inefficient. Not only was much of the heat wasted, some bricks were over-burnt while others were under-burnt. To overcome these problems, purpose built kilns either circular or rectangular in plan, were developed. At first intermittent kilns were used - where the kiln was loaded, fired, cooled and unloaded for each burning. Later on, continuous kilns, where as the name implies, the kiln is kept burning continuously and bricks added and removed in rotation. Until the early 20th century the normal fuel for these brick kilns was coal or coke. The table below gives broad classification of kiln types, those which have been used in Cornwall are indicated in bold type. Downdraught kilns are common. They might be called up and down draught as the hot air entering the kiln rises to the top and is deflected downwards through holes in the floor.

MODE OF USE	INTERMITTENT	CONTINUOUS
MODE OF HEAT DISTRIBUTION AND KILN TYPES	SINGLE CHAMBER KILNS Downdraught - **Beehive, Rectangular** Updraught - *Scotch*, Suffolk Horizontal draught - **Newcastle**	MULTI-CHAMBER KILN **Hoffman**, Belgian, Tunnel

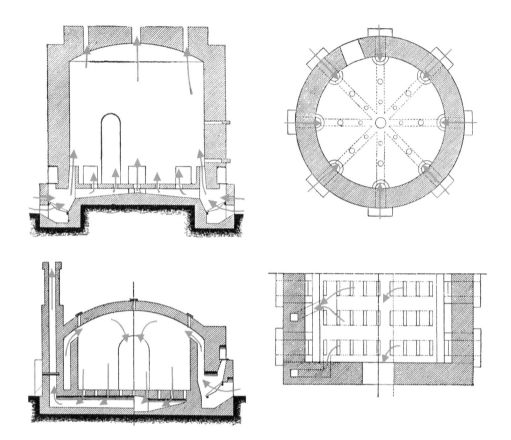

Two early types of kiln showing the heat flow paths during firing. Variations of these are known in Cornwall (see later).
Top Row: *Updraught Beehive Kiln* - Left: *Section* Right: *Plan*
Bottom Row: *Downdraught Rectangular Kiln* - Left: *Section* Right: *partial plan*
After Bourry, 1926Ed., p. 221, Figs. 144 & 145.

Multi-chambered kilns which allowed a continuous rotational burn were patented in the early 1840's. The most famous and widely used of this type was the circular Hoffman Kiln of German design, patented in the United Kingdom by Humphrey Chamberlin in 1859. A rectangular version known as the Belgian kiln was designed by Hoffman in 1870, only one possible example, at Bealeswood (see p.58), is known in the county.

The capacity of the various kilns is quite variable. For example an up-draught Scotch kiln could burn between 20,000 and 50,000 bricks at one burn, while the more efficient downdraught kiln could burn up to 100,000 bricks. These figures should be compared to the clamp in which about 40,000 bricks were the norm, although very large clamps could contain up to 100,000 bricks, but with a large wastage. A modern gas-fired continuous kiln can produce 3.5 million bricks per week.

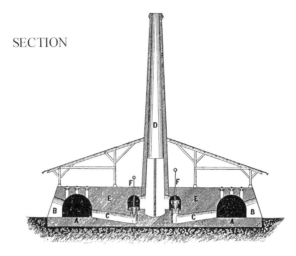

SECTION

PLAN

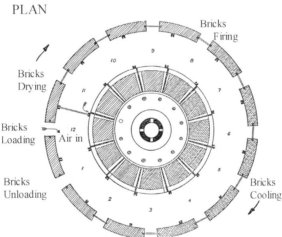

Section and plan of a circular Hoffman Kiln as used in some Cornish brickworks. Redrawn from various sources. In this type of kiln bricks progress clockwise. Airflow and firing proceeds anticlockwise so that the function of the chambers rotates - loading, firing, cooling, emptying.

2.3 CORNISH 19th CENTURY BRICK MAKING

We are fortunate that a s number of specific accounts of brick making in Cornwall have been published, which give some detail of the methods and the equipment used. One example is a record of a visit by E. M. Crofts, to several brickworks in West Cornwall toward the end of the 19th century. This was published in 'The Cornishman', 10/05/1883 and is one of a series of articles he wrote under the pseudonym of 'Ouit', describing the industries of the area around Penzance [2]. He wrote as follows:

BRICKMAKING AROUND PENZANCE 1883

"The mode of manufacture adopted at these works is the same, to all intents and purposes, as that followed in other parts of the country, but a short description will be admissible (sic) here.

The clay is first exposed to the air for a specified time and afterwards, by means of water, is separated from the small stones which, if left in the clay, would cause the brick to split. The next operation is that of 'pugging" or mixing the clay well together, and incorporating it thoroughly with the particular substance which may be added.

The pugging-mill is a conical-shaped wooden tub, having the larger end upwards, with an upright revolving shaft passing through the middle, armed with a number of steel blades, which cut and knead the clay and force it through the mill, which is constantly being turned from the top by a projecting beam, worked, in the present instance, by horsepower. The clay, after passing through the mill [a pug mill], issues from the a hole in the bottom; and thus prepared it is given over into "the hands of the potter to fashion it as he will."

The brick-maker stands at a low bench, and holds in his hands the mould with which to form the bricks. This consists of a square framework of wood, without top or bottom, the art of the workman consisting in striking a piece of clay with such force into it as completely to fill it, and then adeptly striking off the superfluous quantity, and turning out the brick in a barrow placed near him. The expedition of the brick-maker is surprising, and watching him turn out brick after brick, with a very short interval between each, one has a graphic illustration of how "practise makes perfect."

The moulder, I should state, is generally provided with a vessel of water, placed on the bench, into which he dips the mould preparatory to each brick being moulded, to prevent the clay sticking. Sometimes, however, the mould is merely sprinkled with sand between the making of each brick The former process is commonly called "stop moulding," the latter "pallet moulding". The bottom of the mould, termed the stock-board, which is secured to the bench, has a piece of projecting wood called "a kick," fastened to the upper side, to make a hollow in the brick for the sake of lightness and to leave a bed for the mortar.

When the moulder has turned out a barrow load of bricks they are wheeled away, either to the open field and piled up loose in walls and covered with straw, or taken to the drying shed. When they are sufficiently dried, they are next stacked in the kiln and burnt. The kiln is a very simple and inexpensive structure, being a rectangular chamber, built out of old brick, with a narrow doorway at each end and narrow fire holes (sic) lined with fire-brick, in the side walls, exactly opposite each other. Sometimes the fire is made to pass right through the body of the bricks: there are several modes of burning employed. A kiln of bricks takes 72 hours to complete the burning process, and the furnaces in this time consume about seven tons of coal.

At Tregoning-hill (sic) there is one kiln, at Tresowes one, at Wheal Grey two, and at New Town two, each of the ordinary capacity, i.e. capable of holding about 20,000 bricks." [3]

The surviving brick kilns at both Tregonning Hill and Wheal Grey are circular beehive kilns and not rectangular as mentioned in the above account.

Another important eye witness account, is given in the Mining Journal of March 25th and April 8th 1876, as part of a description of the Cornwall Chemical Company's operation at Greenhill in the Tamar Valley. This gives considerable detail and sub-headings have been added to the original text for easier reading.

BRICKMAKING AT GREENHILL 1876

RAW MATERIALS Clay, Quartz and Felspar

"Hence occur the various kinds of fire-bricks in the market, ranging from the Dinas brick, which contains 99 percent. of silica (being made up of pure silica rock ground to powder and mixed with a trace of lime to fuse the particles together), through the Ganister, Garnkirk, Glenboig, Lee Moor, and other kinds, down to the Stourbridge, which contains about 55 per cent of silica. If then, a bed of fire clay were to be found in close proximity to a deposit of pure silica rock, it is evident that any kind of firebrick could be made by simply mixing, the two materials together in the required proportion. Such a happy juxtaposition of elements, however, had never been discovered to exist previous to the commencement of the Greenhill Works, and it was reserved for the general manager of the Cornwall Chemical Company to point out that the decomposed granite found on their land supplied the desideratum in question. He showed that the decomposition affected the crystals of felspar alone, and that the crystals of quartz contained perfectly hard, and therefore that the felspar might be removed from the quartz by simple washing with water. The granite would then be split up into a mass of pure silica and a mass of feldspar or fire clay, and by using either separately, or combining them in chosen proportions, any required description of fire brick might be made. This suggestion has now been carried into practice, and the result is that the fire brick manufactory of the Cornwall Chemical Company is positively unrivalled as regards the varieties of the fire goods it is capable of producing a result of great commercial importance, seeing that every large consumer of fire-bricks requires several distinct varieties, and must naturally prefer to deal with a company that can produce all rather than have to buy separate parcels from several makers. Another important consequence of the separation of the granite into quartz and feldspar is to enable the rock to be converted into a powerful chemical agent for the utilisation of certain, metallic ores, which would otherwise be thrown aside as valueless. To this we shall revert when we come to the chemical department of the works.

CLAY PREPARATION Using Crushing and Weathering

Having seen the clay excavated from the quarry we will now follow it through the various manufacturing operations to which it is subjected. Proceeding up the incline into the grinding house we find that the wagons of raw material are brought to a standstill on a large platform, in which is a funnel shaped opening leading to the crushing mill. This consists of two pairs of cast iron rollers Placed one under the other, and so arranged that the upper set crushes the material into coarse fragments, while the lower reduces these to a comparatively fine powder, which is then stored in large heaps under the platform to "weather," as it is termed. The process of "weathering," is very important in most fictile industries. It is practically the exposure of the material in a finely divided condition to the action of atmospheric agencies, assisted by periodically turning over the mass with spades and sprinkling it with water. The effect of this is to promote the disintegration of the particles, and to render the mass more or less plastic, according to the length of time that the weathering is allowed to continue, and in proportion as perfect plasticity is attained the moulding of the articles desired to be formed call be effected with greater facility and truth. Another advantage of complete disintegration is that the material is thereby rendered more dense and homogeneous, and the moulded goods when subjected to the intense heat necessary for burning them are less likely to warp or crack from unequal expansion and contraction, or to become porous from the formation of air holes.

The crushing mill is only employed for two varieties of clay, that is to say first, for the decomposed granite just as it comes from the quarry without any preliminary treatment; and, secondly, for the disintegrated killas or clay slate which forms the overburthen or covering of the granite, and which has to be cleared away before the latter can be excavated. Until recently this overburthen was regarded as altogether useless, and was trammed away to a vast spoil bank occupying a large area in the centre or the quarry, and interfering with the systematic removal of the fire-clay. It occurred, however, to the general manager of the company that this spoil bank contained the elements of ordinary brick earth, and that it might be possible to use it for the manufacture of red bricks for building purposes. He accordingly instituted the necessary experiments, and had the satisfaction of finding his views fully borne out, so that now not only do the company make their own building bricks, which they had previously been obliged to purchase at a price exceeding 50s. per thousand, but they are also supplying large quantities to the neighbourhood of the works at a considerable profit, and at the same time they have ceased to be incommoded by the overburthen of their fire clay.

GRINDING using edge runner mills for superior firebricks

We have said that a portion only of the decomposed granite is passed direct through the crushing mill as ordinary fire clay. The remainder is carefully washed, and by this means separated into fine china clay on the one hand, and into a coarse silica sand on the other. We thus find on the clay floor no less than four varieties of raw material – fire-clay, brick earth, china clay, and silica sand; and these are treated separately or mixed together in various proportions, according to the several purposes which the manufactured goods are destined to subserve. For building bricks the crushed and weathered overburthen is sent direct to the moulders, as also is the crushed and weathered fire clay for ordinary fire bricks; but for superior articles there intervenes an additional apparatus in the shape of a massive pair of edge runners, driven by the same engine that works the crushing mill and quarry incline. Under these edge-runners the several materials can be ground and rubbed down to any degree of fineness, and it is found that even the ordinary fire clay may be thus made to acquire a plasticity and homogeneity sufficient to produce a greatly increased power of withstanding the action of fire, and especially of alternate heating and cooling. So, too, with the silica sand, which if simply crushed cannot readily be made to sufficiently cohere in the processes of moulding and drying unless such a proportion of lime be used as to seriously injure its refractory qualities; whereas, if thoroughly triturated (ground) beneath, the edge-runners, it may be moulded and handled almost without any cementing material whatever.

BRICK MOULDING by the sand stock system

The moulding of the bricks is carried out using what is known as the "sand stock" system, so called from the use of sand to prevent the clay from adhering to the mould, whereas when water is used for this purpose the bricks are known as "slop stocks," The moulder stands at a wooden bench or table, and is assisted by three boys. One brings the clay from the weathering pile and shovels it into a heap upon the moulding table; the second, with an instrument composed of a curved piece of hoop iron between two upright handles, cuts from the mass a succession of lumps of clay about large enough for a brick, and rolls them, into "balls" for the moulder; while the third is kept occupied in arranging the moulded bricks on a large barrow, and in wheeling them away to the drying house. On receiving the lump of clay from the "baller" the moulder sprinkles (sic) some dry sand in his mould, which is an oblong frame of iron, lined with brass, and fitting on an iron foot plate fastened to the bench. He then lifts the ball in both hands, and dashes it with considerable force into the mould, which it rather more than fills, and he removes the excess by passing a wooden striker across the upper edges of the mould. By a dexterous motion he next slides rather than lifts the mould from the foot plate, and deposits the contained brick upon one of the "pallets" with which his assistant has covered the surface of the light framework constituting the barrow, and which are simply thin oak boards, rather longer and wider than a brick, and used for handling the soft bricks without injury to their shape. Having thus laid the brick down he can draw off the mould, and fix it again on the foot plate ready to receive another ball.

DRYING AND PRESSING OF BRICKS

The bricks when thus moulded are laid in long rows upon the door of the drying house. This is a very large building, with a series of furnaces at one end and chimneys at the other, the flame and heated products of combustion passing through flucs covered with square tiles of fire clay, which form the floor. The fires are fed for the most part with the small coal and cinder obtained from the stoking pits of the kilns, and are kept continuously alight. By this means the temperature of the drying house is raised to summer-heat all the year round, and the moulded bricks in the course of from 21 to 48 hours are rendered sufficiently dry and hard for pressing. To carry out this process a machine is employed consisting of two jaws, one fixed and the other movable, between which the ends of an iron bar revolving horizontally on a pivot attached to the frame of the press are alternately brought. Each of these ends is fitted with a frame similar to that employed in moulding the bricks, but the foot plate or die is free to move upwards and downwards inside the frame. The fixed jaw of the machine is also provided with a plate or die fitting the frame, and the dies are furnished with projecting letters or devices for whatever names or trade marks the bricks are desired to bear. A boy gathers up the rough dried bricks from the floor of the drying house, and wheels them to the pressman, who places them one by one in the frames, and then, revolving the frame into position between the jaws, seizes the projecting spokes of a large wheel attached to the press, and with a quick powerful jerk actuates a knee lever, which lifts the lower jaw. A pressure of about 5 tons is thus communicated to the lower die, and the brick contained in the frame is rendered thoroughly solid, hard, and perfect in shape. On the lever being released it falls, and the bar is spun wound for the other end to come between the jaws, while the frame containing the pressed brick remains immediately above an iron pin, which is caused to rise at pleasure by a treadle at the foot of the press. A boy known as the "taker off" then works the treadle, and the iron pin forces the lower die through the frame. The pressed brick is thus lifted out, and is immediately removed by means of a loose frame or "grip," and placed on a pallet as before to be wheeled away to a second drying house, where it remains until it becomes dry and hard enough for handling and stacking in the kilns.

Where bulky articles, such as lumps and tiles, have to be made the processes of moulding and pressing above described cannot be employed. In lieu thereof a wooden frame of the requisite dimensions is placed upon the drying floor, and carefully filled with clay, which is thoroughly beaten and pressed into every corner, and after being "struck" has its surface finished with it smoothing trowel and impressed with any desired mark or brand. The frame is then lifted away, and set down on the floor at a little distance to be again filled, and so on, the moulded articles being allowed to remain until they are sufficiently hard and dry for the kilns.

FIRING using beehive Scrivener kilns

We next come to the burning of the fire goods. On leaving the drying houses we see in front of us a circle of eight massive domes, constructed of brickwork, and bound round by wide bands of wrought iron. Each of these structures has an arched doorway, on entering which we find ourselves in a large circular chamber, with a domed roof, and with an immense tube of brickwork projecting from the centre of the floor, and rising more than halfway to the roof. Clambering up so as to peep down this tube we see by the light streaming in from an aperture at the summit of the dome that it leads to a vast fire grate far below, from whence volleys of the fiercest flames must often be discharged if we are to judge by the semi fused appearance of the inside of the tube. Looking at the dome overhead, we also see where these flames strike and reverberate upon all sides, filling the kiln from roof to floor, until they finally make their exit through a series of small holes ranged round the chamber floor, and leading into the flue which conducts to the chimney stack standing in the centre of the circle formed by the eight kilns. The fires are tended from a stoking pit excavated beneath each kiln, and capacious enough to hold 10 tons or more of coal, and a shelter-box for the fireman.

Each kiln holds about 20,000 bricks, lumps, tiles, &c,, which are stacked in circular rows and diagonally between the circles, so as to form it multitude of channels for the passage of the flame. When the kiln is full the doorway is bricked up and covered over tightly with a coating of fire clay, while the test holes in the roof are also plugged. At first the bricks are too " green" - they contain too much moisture to bear being fired. They are, therefore, "steamed" by opening a connection with some kiln that has been fired and is now cooling. The heated air from the latter is thus forced to traverse the green bricks on its way to the chimney stack, and all along the contents of the newly charged kiln become divested of every trace of moisture. All the flue connections are then closed with the exception of those leading from the fire and to the stack, and the fire is lighted. The heat is raised very gradually, and the interior of the kiln is constantly observed by withdrawing loose bricks placed for the purpose in the roof and doorway. At length when a full white heat is seen at all parts of the kiln the fire is urged to its uttermost by feeding it with large selected lumps of coal, and a torrent of flame is discharged through the kiln until it can just be observed on lifting the damper in the flue at the foot of the stack. Testing rods are then introduced to measure the shrinkage which has taken place in the contents of the kiln, and so soon as this has reached the calculated amount the fires are drawn and the kiln left to cool a process which requires some, five or six days. This accomplished, the kilns are opened, and their contents drawn and loaded into wagons on the railway which surrounds the kilns, and which communicates by a self-acting incline with the siding into the main line forming the northern boundary of the company's premises. The kilns here described are known as Scrivener kilns, and do their work very well if carefully fired. They require, however, a somewhat large proportion of fuel from 14 to 16 cwts. per 1000 bricks - and the fuel has to consist of the best household coal, seeing that the efficacy of the burning depends upon the volume of flame, which must be sufficient to thoroughly fill all parts of the kiln.

FIRING using Batchelor kilns

Several attempts have been elsewhere made to improve upon them, but at the Greenhill Works they have been adopted in the place of another system which the original proprietor of the works had chosen. These were what are called Batchelor kilns, and consist of circular structures with domed roofs, heated by a number of separate fires placed at intervals round the exterior wall, and communicating with hollow linings or pockets on the interior, from whence the flames were discharged, and reverberated (sic) into the centre of the kiln where the exit flue was situated. It had been thought that by dividing the fires a more equal distribution of heat could be effected, and that by shortening the distance between the fire and the exit flue a diminution might be made in the required volume of flame, but in practice it was found that neither of these advantages was attained. The pockets took up much valuable space in the kilns, and hindered the flame from reaching a large portion of the bricks, so that in order to fairly burn a kiln the fires had to be forced to such all extent that the pockets themselves wore constantly being burnt out or damaged. The repairs thus entailed were not only very expensive, but led to great delays, and in the end the whole of the eight kilns were altered to the Scrivener system.

EXPERIMENTAL FIRING WITH PRODUCER GAS

At one time the experiment of burning bricks by gas was tried at the Greenhill Works. Two Siemens' [Producer Gas] generators were erected and connected with two of the kilns by the necessary gas and air channels. These led into the central fire tube, and the supply of both gas and air could be regulated so as to admit of perfect combustion, as in a Bunsen's burner, being attained. It is evident that the conditions of economy and efficiency were here combined. The gag was produced from slack and small coal. One fireman could attend the two generators, which were sufficient for the eight kilns. There was no waste of heat, material, or time by continual lighting and extinction. The flame was not produced until it had actually reached its work. The rapidity and completeness of the combustion were under perfect control, and the volume of flame could be augmented or diminished at pleasure, and to any required extent. Two kilns of bricks are actually burned in this manner; and, although the bricks came out ruddier red in colour, and not sufficiently hard, yet the experiment was so far successful as to show the practicability of burning bricks by gas at a great saving over the present system. It was found, however, that local prejudice was opposed to the innovation, and that the engineer under whose charge the work had been carried out was not sufficiently competent, and accordingly the attempt was abandoned."

Elsewhere at this time there were several experiments with producer gas which were carried out by some mines and china clay works, but like those reported from Greenhill, they were found to be unsuccessful.

These two documents illustrate the broad picture of brick making in Cornwall and include some indication of the equipment used. Other accounts of brick making in the south west include: Nichols [4], who describes the operations of the Tamar Brick and Fireclay Company, Gunnislake and that of Turpin [5], describing the Lee Moor Brickworks in Devon. One other contemporary document which is worthy of attention is a handbill advertising the sale by auction of equipment used at the Tolcarne Brickworks, Newquay in 1896. The list of equipment gives a further insight into the machinery used in a small Cornish brickworks, toward the end of the 19th century.

April 3, 1896.]   NEWQUAY VISITORS' NOTES AND DIRECTORY.   583

To Brickmakers and Builders.

MR. SILAS RICKEARD

Will SELL BY AUCTION, at

TOLCARNE BRICKWORKS, NEWQUAY,

ON

FRIDAY, 10th April, at 2.30 p.m.,

A Valuable Lot of

PLANT, BRICKMAKING MACHINERY, AND BUILDING MATERIALS,

COMPRISING :

A most useful Horizontal **ENGINE**, by Tangye, 8-in. cylinder, 15-in. stroke.

One 8-ton Cornish Boiler and Mountings.

8-ft. 6-in. Perforated Clay-grinding Pan, with two rolls 45cwt. each.

A fine semi-dry Brick Machine (nearly new),

By Henry Tuke and Sons, Leeds, will make **10,000 a day.**

A good Pug Hand Press, Cutting-off Table,

$2\frac{1}{2}$in. Pump, Chain Pump, and a variety of other useful articles.

Also the Brick and Stone **Work** of the Kilns, Stacks and Sheds,

Comprising some Hundreds of Thousands of valuable Fire and Building Bricks and Materials.

Dated Trenance, Newlyn East, and Newquay, 20th March, 1896.

Hand bill announcing the sale of brick making equipment.

Field work throughout Cornwall has revealed that very little remains of the equipment used to manufacture bricks. The survival of brick kilns on the other hand, although spasmodic, is more frequent. We therefore have to rely heavily on documentary evidence, and in particular the writings quoted earlier for information relating to the equipment used by the industry. A survey of these and other surviving documents suggests that most brick works used the standard equipment as discussed in the first section of this Chapter. Some would be locally made, while some would have been purchased from specialist manufacturers such as Henry Tuke & Sons. of Leeds, (see sale handbill for the Tolcarne brickworks, opposite). Evidence from Bealeswood Brickworks suggests that even the steam engines used to drive the equipment were imported.

One locally made item was a horse driven pug mill made by Bartle's Foundry, Pool, Redruth, although we have not been able to find any specific record of its use. Needless to say none have survived. As crusher rolls, were a common product of Cornish iron foundries, it seems likely that these were manufactured locally although again we have no records or survivors (crusher rolls were a common piece of equipment used in mineral dressing, but again no Cornish examples survive). The only surviving piece of equipment known, is the pug mill at Carbis Brick Works. This machine was driven by a belt drive connected to a water-wheel which was some distance away and is similar to that illustrated earlier (page 20) made

A one horse power pug mill, made in Cornwall by Bartle of Carn Brea.
None have survived, although there is a model in Camborne Museum.

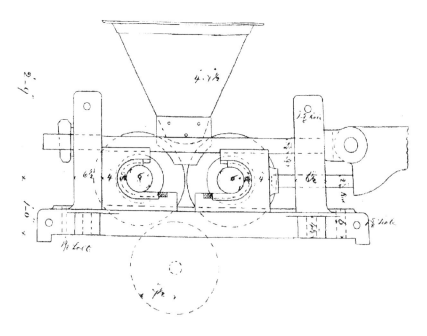

Side elevation of Cornish crushing rolls.

Carbis Brickworks: combined crusher rolls and pug mill. There is no makers mark.

by Edwards & Jones of London. At Carbis the feed hopper is missing. The end of the Archimedes screw which mixed and forced the clay through the barrel can be seen but the extrusion plate through which a continuous slab of brick was formed has gone.

Early hacks used for the first stage of drying were temporary and it wasn't until underfloor heating was introduced, that permanent brick dries were built. One survivor is at Carkeet where a granite rubble building used to have a water-wheel operated pug mill and moulding shop at one end and a heated drying area at the other. The dry occupies about two thirds of the building and has six fireplaces along the west wall. It is assumed that the floor of the building was formed from porous tiles probably graded in a similar fashion to those in a clay dry.

The brick dry, Carkeet brickworks. The fireplaces are visible in the vegetation at the base of the wall. The pug mill and moulding shop was at the far end of the building.

All of the types of kiln mentioned earlier have been used by Cornish brick makers. The majority of surviving examples are what are generally termed "Beehive" Kilns which used the updraught principle to distribute the heat. As noted in the first of the accounts quoted (p. 36 last paragraph), two types were in general use, Batchelor Kilns which were a circular version of the downdraught rectangular kiln (page 28, lower) and Scrivener Kilns (page 42, top). The principal difference between the two is that in the Batchelor Kiln there are several fireplaces at intervals around the perimeter with baffles directing the heat upward into the kiln, whereas in the Scrivener Kiln there was one fireplace beneath the kiln and the heat was led into the kiln by a central flue, waste gases passing out through openings in the floor around the perimeter and thence to the chimney.

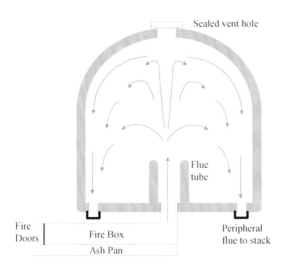

Section through a "Scrivener Kiln", a type of Beehive kiln frequently used in Cornwall, as used for example at Carbis Brickworks.

"Batchelor Kiln", Grampound Road Brickworks, Halezy

Examples of Cornish Brick Kilns.
Left: *"Scrivener Kiln", Carbis Brickworks photographed c.1907*
Right: *Rectangular, downdraught Kiln, Greenhill*

Other types of intermittent kilns were also used. The remains of three rectangular downdraught kilns can be found in undergrowth at the site of Bealeswood Brick Works, while at Carkeet a small, 6 feet 6 inches (1.98 metres) by 9 feet (2.75 metres), Newcastle Kiln has survived. Scotch kilns have been recorded but none have been found extant.

Continuous circular Hoffman Kilns were also used in Cornwall as for example at St. Day and at Dimson near Gunnislake in the Tamar Valley (see page 44).

It is difficult to find output figures for Cornish brickyards as we often are only given the number of bricks which could be fired in the kiln at one time, thus in the West Cornwall example quoted earlier we are told that the kilns mentioned could hold 20,000 bricks. In the Tolcarne hand bill it is noted that the brick making machine which is to be sold, is capable of making 10,000 bricks per day. A similar notice of sale for Par brickworks in 1928 suggests that their machine made 8,000 bricks per day. Other published figures note that St. Day Brickworks produced 1.5 million bricks in 1867, which was reduced to one million the following year owing to the stagnation of the market. In the 1960's and just before closure, the North Cornwall firm which operated Whitstone Brickworks was producing 15,000 bricks each week.

Examples of Cornish Hoffman Kilns illustrated in 19th century photographs.
Top: *St. Day Brickworks. The Hoffman kiln no longer exists.*
Bottom: *Plymouth Works, Dimson, Tamar Valley. This kiln is now a pile of rubble.*

2.4 THE WORK FORCE

Typically the 18th & 19th century brickyard work force would comprise men, women and children of both sexes. The children were employed to carry out menial tasks such as carrying clay from the pug mill to the moulding bench, attending to the kiln fires or sifting ashes. During the 19th century the employment of children in brickyards and elsewhere led to many protests by reformers and numerous articles were published drawing attention to this state of affairs.

An illustration from Pyne's Microcosm (1714), showing a mixed group people of differing ages and sex (perhaps an itinerant family), carrying out the early stages of brick making.

The report of a visit in the 1860's by members of the Children's Employment Commission on the situation at the Bealeswood Works at Gunnislake, is particularly damning of the conditions they found (Appendix to the 5th Report of the Children's Employment Commission, 1865 – 66, p.148). Of the 32 men and boys at Bealeswood they found that seven were under the age of 13 years and six were aged between 13 and 18 years. Four girls were employed one aged 17 years and the others between 12 and 14 years. Many of the children had never attended school and could neither read nor write. Alcoholic drink was a problem with the children, some of whom regularly got drunk. One 8 year old boy whose job it was to drive the horse turning the pug mill was noted because of his use of bad language. He was paid 4d. (less than 2p) a day. During the summer months, he was expected to work between 16 and 20 hours a day. Also mentioned is the 17 year old girl, who was employed as an off-bearer, a very heavy task involving moving the wet bricks from the moulding bench to the

drying area. For this work she could earn up to £1 – 0 – 0d (£1.00) per week, working
5½ days and at least 100 hours a week during the summer months.

A Victorian reformer, George Smith of Coalville, Leicestershire was a fervent
campaigner against the employment of children in brickworks. In 1871 he published
a pamphlet entitled "The Cry of the Children from the Brickyards of England". One
consequence of this was the publication of a number articles in 'The Graphic' under the
heading "Brickyard Children". In these, a desperate picture of the lives of children in the
brickyards was painted. To emphasize the need for reform, some of the iniquities in the
situation were highlighted by means of illustration. Some of the illustrations accompanying
the articles in 'The Graphic', are reproduced opposite. More information on this topic can
be gained from articles published in the newsletters of the British Brick Society [6].

Many brick makers were itinerant, moving from town to town, wherever brick-
makers were wanted. In Dickens' novel, "Bleak House" [7] for example, the trials and
tribulations of two 'brick making' families who seem to have moved regularly between
St. Albans and London for their work, forms a subplot to the main story. In Cornwall
during the 18th and 19th centuries this pattern of itinerant workers can also be found,
when a number of small brick-making enterprises were started for the building of, or
extension to houses such as Heligan and Trelowarren. After the development of more
permanent works in the middle of the 19th century, workers continued to move from
brickworks to brickworks. Those who were highly skilled were in demand to help solve
teething problems at new works and we shall comment on a number of specific cases
later, when we consider individual Cornish brickworks.

There is little information, other than that already quoted, regarding the payment of
workers employed in this industry in Cornwall. We know for example that for temporary
ventures, such as those set up for house building projects, brick-makers worked to an
agreed price per thousand usable bricks produced, while others had fixed rates for a
particular job, such as searching for suitable clay.

In the County of Bedfordshire some of the agreements made between land owners
and others with individual brick-makers or labourers have been recorded by Alan Cox
in his survey of Bedfordshire Brickworks [8]. In one example he sets out the agreement
made between 3 brick makers and a farmer to run a small brickworks on his farm. The
men agreed a rate which they would be paid for the saleable bricks and draining tiles
produced, with the proviso that they would dig and cart the clay to the brickyard, mould
the bricks and/or draining tiles and fire them in a kiln. They were also obliged to load
customer's carts. The farmer for his part would supply the necessary coal and straw, as
well as horses to work the pug mill and fetch any sand required. He reserved the right
to specify the types, quantities and sizes of both brick and draining tiles to be made,
also agreeing to advance money for necessary expenditure once every two weeks [9].

'Brickyard Children' From "The Graphic", June 1871.
Top: *Carrying clay from the pug mill.* Bottom Left: *Firing the kiln.*
Bottom Right: *Sifting ashes to recycle unburnt coal.*
Notice the ragged clothes and bare feet of the children.

Other Bedfordshire examples referred to by Cox [10], show that a fortnights work for one man, digging and wheeling clay at 8d (approximately 3p) per yard [11], brought a remuneration of £1-0-0d (£1.00). In another case involving the turning clay to aid weathering, the rate was 1¾d (just less than 1p) a yard, so that a labourer turning 1563 yards of clay, earned £11-4-0d (£11.20), (the time this took was not specified).

Returning to Cornwall, the information relating to the payment of employees is somewhat sparse and the recorded figures are gathered together in the table below.

Date	Works	Rate	Value Today	Worker
c.1860	Bealeswood	4d (day)	£3.85	boy 8 years
c.1860	Bealeswood	£1 (week)	£42.00	girl 17 years
1877	St. Day	2/4d (10 hr.day)	£27.50	man
1908	St. Day	7/6d (week)	£15.40	boy 14 years
1922	Burthy	8/- (week)	£19.00	boy 17 years
1924	Carbis	12/6d (week)	£13.00	boy 14 years

Rates of pay at Cornish brickworks [12]. Normally workers would be expected to work a 5½ day week, but the hours worked could vary, being considerably more during the summer. The value today given is an approximate comparative weekly wage, taking into account changes in value of the pound between the date quoted and the year 2000.

END NOTES

1   Thurlow . 1994 The Tunnel Kiln at Dewerstone. Plymouth Mineral & Mining
    Club Newsletter. Vol.14 No. 2, Nov. 1994
2   "The Industries of Penzance and its Neighbourhood" No. vii, - *Our Brickworks*
3   The author corrected this statement a week later (17/05/1883), pointing out that
    there were no brickworks at Tresowes.
4   Nichols B. 1972 The Tamar Brick and Fireclay Company. Industrial Archaeology
    Vol.9, pages 251 & 253
5   Turpin P.L.A. The passing of the Lee Moor Brick Works. English China Clay
    Review, p10-11, Summer 1965
6   British Brick Society Information No. 19, Nov. 1979
7   Dickens C. "Bleak House" 1994 Edition, Pages 286-287, 392-393, 576-577 &
    714-715
8   Cox A. 1979 "Survey of Bedfordshire: Brick making a History and Gazetteer."
    Bedfordshire County Council/R.C.H.M.
9   Ibid. p.20-21
10 Ibid. p.22
11 It is assumed that the 'yard' in this context was 1 cubic yard (0.765 cubic metres).
12 Conversion is base on 240d in £1-0-0d Sterling, equivalent to 100p or £1.00.

CHAPTER 3

BRICK MAKING SITES - EAST CORNWALL

Details so far as they are known of the brick making sites in Cornwall, are given in the following 4 chapters. Chapters 3 - 5 deal with separate geographical areas of the county as indicated on the map at the start of Chapter 1. Chapter 6 is concerned with estate brickyards and some smaller less important sites. As far as possible maps showing the layout of individual works, many copied from early 20th century large scale Ordnance Survey maps, are included. These maps are not to scale unless otherwise indicated and are normally oriented with north at the top. Although national grid references are given for each site, some sketch maps have been included to assist in locating individual works as well as showing their geographical relationships.

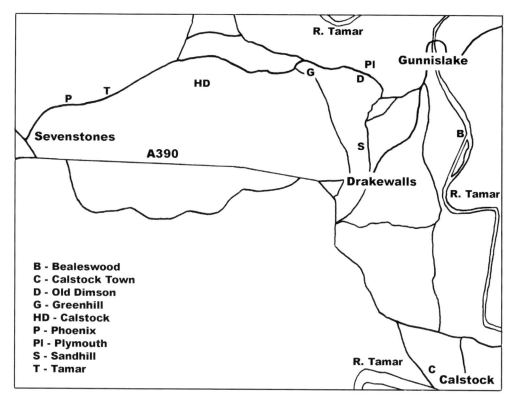

Sketch map showing the approximate locations of the Cornish brick making sites in the Tamar Valley region, discussed with grid references in the text.

3.1 TAMAR VALLEY

The Phoenix Vitrified Paving & Firebrick Works - 4.5 km. NE of Callington
Grid Reference SX395715
These works which started in 1864 were short lived, the operator terminating the lease
after 9 years. The Phoenix Works used two clays: a decomposed white killas with about
3% Fe_2O_3 and a red coloured killas with about 15% Fe_2O_3. These were dug from clay
pits close by. After preparation the bricks were fired in a row of 5 beehive kilns. The
two clays gave rise to white and blue bricks, which were fired to give a vitrified, glazed
finish. Examples of these bricks can be seen around the base of Venning's Fountain,
Callington (see Chapter 7, p.132). Vitreous paving bricks and glazed terracotta tiles were
also produced [1]. Phoenix terracotta tiles can be found on buildings in the area, as well
as in Brighton, where the architect Thomas Lainson specified its use on buildings he
designed. The site was cleared and occupied c.1910 by the Phoenix Pleasure grounds.
It is now a breakers yard.

Brickmark: PHOENIX

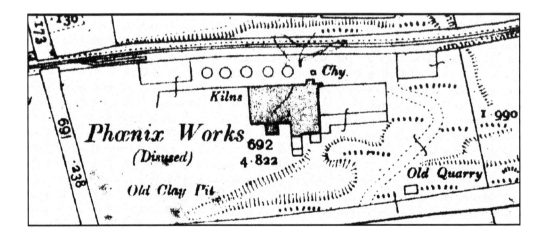

Phoenix Vitrified Paving & Firebrick Works © Crown Copyright 1907

*Test brick from the Phoenix works. It is
4¼" wide x 1¾" thick x 2¼" long. A slice of
brick placed in the kiln so it can be easily
removed by a poker using the central hole to
check whether firing is complete.*

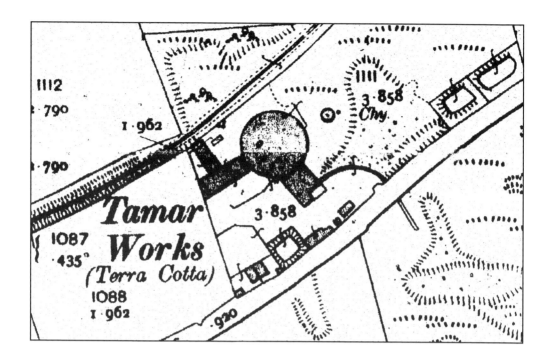

Tamar Firebrick & Clay Company Works © Crown Copyright 1907

The Tamar Firebrick & Clay Company – 4.5 km. NE of Callington, between Cox's Park and Chilsworthy
Grid Reference SX400717
The Tamar Firebrick Company works was established in 1871 and the clay, a decomposed elvan, was obtained from a quarry across the road from the works, to which it was connected by an adit with a tramway. A large Hoffman kiln with 16 compartments was built here (centre of map) and was used to fire large quantities of firebricks and, more importantly, terracotta tiles. See Nichols for a more complete description of the operation [2].

The works survived until 1935 with a change of title to the Tamar Brickwork & Potteries Ltd. and around this time power was supplied for the works by a 100 BHP Ruston horizontal oil engine. Chemical stoneware Chapter 7, p.147) was also made in the later years. The works has been entirely demolished and the quarry back filled, leaving the blocked south entrance to the adit as the only remains, marking the site. As before, examples of the decorative terracotta produced here can be seen on buildings in the district. White coloured firebrick was also manufactured here. These bricks had no frog.

Brickmark: TAMAR

All that remains today of the Tamar Firebrick & Clay Cos. works,
the top of the entrance to the adit with dated keystone (1871).

Some Tamar Valley brickmarks. Wheal Martyn China Clay
Museum collection.
Top Left: *Tamar* Top Right: *Dimson* Bottom Left: *Greenhill* Bottom Right:
Westlake (Greenhill or Bealeswood).

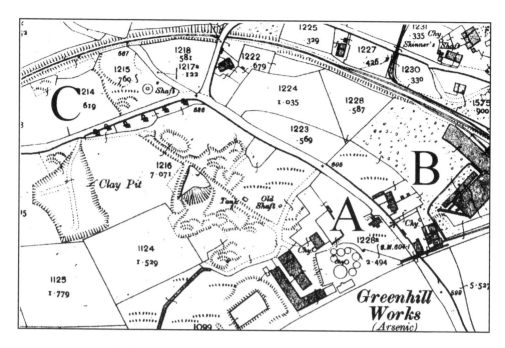

Greenhill Works, Chilsworthy© Crown Copyright 1907

Greenhill Works and Hill Westlake Works - near. Drakewalls, Chilsworthy
Grid Reference SX420717 (A on map) and SX418719 (C on map)
In Chapter 2 we quoted verbatim an article published in the Mining Journal of 1876, describing this brickworks (marked **A** on map), which was associated with the Greenhill Arsenic Works (B on map). Both the brickworks and the arsenic works were owned by the Cornwall Chemical Co. and, as can be seen on the accompanying map, the two works were separated the by the Calstock - Chilsworthy road. The brickworks itself was situated to the west of the road, while the arsenic works are to the east. It has been suggested that the brick making here started as early as 1873, with a relatively large clay pit being recorded to the NW of the works by 1907. There were 8 Scrivener beehive kilns which replaced the earlier Batchelor kilns on the site (marked just below A on the map) All have now been demolished, although their footprints can still be made out. On the north side of the access road there is the remains of a building which may have been used to dry the bricks.

An incident involving arsenical poisoning at Greenhill brickworks was reported in 1874 [3]. It appears that someone put a barrow load of white oxide of arsenic into the tank which stored the water used by the brick workers to brew their tea. Workers who drank tea made from this water were immediately taken ill and diagnosed as having arsenic poisoning. Fortunately the problem was diagnosed quickly and treatment given so that none of the workers was killed.

Hill Westlake Works (C on map, p.53).

Top: *View of the preparation plant building. The new stonework structure to the right of the stack links the Plastech Ltd. offices to the old building. Note the girder across the road which was designed to carry the tramway from the clay pit.*

Bottom: *A view of the side of one of the rectangular, kilns showing the 7 firing holes. The tile paved coal yard is between the two extant kilns and was originally roofed over.*

Examining the inside of an unused rectangular kiln at Hill Westlakes works. Note that there is no evidence that the kiln had ever been fired. Access by kind permission of Plastech Ltd.

At some point, brick manufacture was taken over by Hill Westlake and a new works was established (location marked **C** on the map), on the north side of the road and opposite the clay pit. The date for this new development is not certain, but must have been between 1907 and 1919.

On this new site a large building to house the preparation plant was built, with a chimney stack at its east end, presumably to service the boilers for a steam engine which would drive the brick making machinery. Nearby at least three rectangular kilns and a Scrivener beehive kiln were also constructed, along with a second chimney. There is no evidence that these kilns were ever connected to a flue and examination suggests that they were never used.

All the buildings mentioned survive except for one rectangular kiln. The girders which would have carried a tramway over the road from the clay pit to the brick preparation plant can still be seen. The whole site is now occupied by Plastech Ltd., who are utilising some of the original buildings

Brickmark: WESTLAKE & GREENHILL

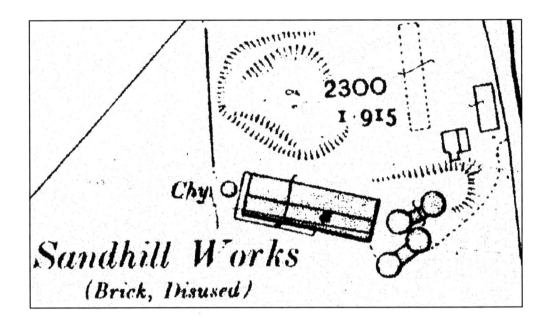

Sandhill Works, Drakewalls © Crown Copyright 1907

Sandhill Works - Drakewalls
Grid Reference SX425711
A small works established about 1860 by B. Johns & Co., of Gunnislake. As can be seen on the accompanying map the brick drying shed and four beehive kilns were built fairly close together. The works was operational until c.1900.

Of the four kilns, the two southern-most have survived along with the base of the chimney which is now a garden feature. A bungalow has been built over the site of the northern-most pair of kilns The southern-most kiln is now used as a storage shed by the present owners while its neighbour (illustrated opposite), which is only partly in the garden of the property has been bricked up for safety reasons. The site of the brick making and drying building is now occupied by a swimming pool.

The clay pit, just to the north of the brickmaking and drying building is preserved as a sunken garden (opposite).

The main product of this brickworks was a white coloured firebrick made without a frog.

Brickmark: SANDHILL

Bricked-up top section of one of the surviving Sandhill beehive kilns.

The Sandhill Works clay pit now features as a sunken garden.

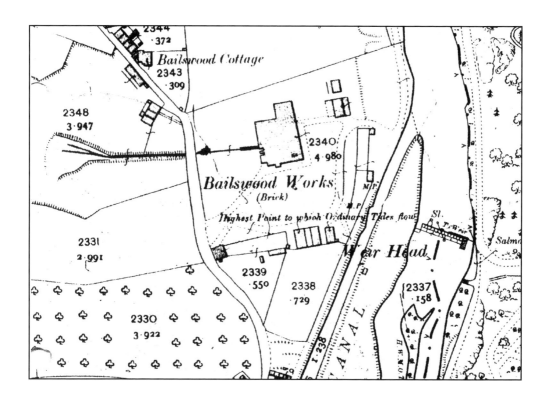

Bealeswood brickworks © Crown Copyright 1907

Bealeswood Brickworks – on River Tamar near Gunnislake
Grid Reference SX435713
Situated adjacent to the Tamar Canal the works was started c.1850 by Thomas Westlake, when it was known by the older name 'Bailswood Works'. It is not clear when the name was changed to 'Bealeswood'. Eventually it became the largest brick works in Cornwall, closing in 1914.

The photograph opposite illustrates the extent of the works showing what appear to be five rectangular downdraught kilns (3 at back beyond the brick drying area and 2 botttom left) as well as a rectangular Hoffman or Belgian kiln (rectangular building centre right in photograph).

At SX436712 are the remains of an engine house, which housed a rotative beam engine. This engine, which was not of Cornish manufacture, drove the machinery on the site and may also have been used to power the tramway used to carry raw material from a clay pit which was situated to the west of the works.

As mentioned earlier (Chapter 2), conditions under which children were employed at these works, were reported on in some detail by the Children's Employment Commission in the 1880's [4].

Today, the site of the brickworks is very boggy and much overgrown. It is now very difficult to locate specific buildings, many of which have completely collapsed and disappeared into the undergrowth and the photograph on p.60 (top) shows what is left of one of several rectangular kilns each 30 feet (9.14 metres) by 15 feet (4.57 metres), which gives some idea of the poor state of the site today. The house (centre right below) is still lived in.

The Westlake bricks are red in colour with no frog.

Brickmarks: BAILSWOOD (early), BEALESWOOD, WESTLAKE

Bealeswood brick works c1900. The rectangular chimney in the centre of the photograph was for the beam engine which drove the brick making machinery. (The photo is also featured by Paige [5]).

Bealeswood brick works in 2004. The remains of a rectangular kiln can just be seen in the undergrowth. Compare this with the preservation of the Sandhill works.

Plymouth Works, Dimson. This building, near what was the entrance to the works, was probably the brickworks managers office or house.

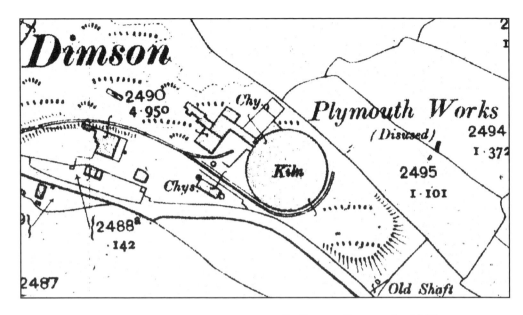

Plymouth Brickworks near Dimson © Crown Copyright 1907

Plymouth Works – North Dimson, near Gunnislake
Grid Reference SX426719
In 1856 this brickworks was listed in Kelly's Directory under the name "J. Bowhay" and in 1873 as the "Dimson Fireclay Company", manager Samuel Lake, . In 1883 and 1889, it is listed as the Plymouth Fireclay Co., manager A.H. Bates. The clay used came from Greenhill and was carried on a 500 yard (457 metres) long spur from the East Cornwall Minerals Railway. The main product were firebricks, although some glazed bricks were also made, which were a novelty for Cornwall as that particular market was dominated by Candy, Devon. The bricks were burnt in a large, circular Hoffman Kiln, which has now been demolished leaving a pile of rubble. The kiln is shown in the centre of the map and a view is illustrated in Chapter 2, p.44 (bottom), which shows this large Hoffman kiln dominating the view.

What appears to have been the managers house survives near the roadside, positioned near what was the entrance to the works. Also surviving are the buttresses carrying the remains of the tramway which was used to carry the clay over the road to the works.

Brickmarks: DIMSON and PLYMOUTH

Brickmark of the Plymouth Works on a broken brick. Wheal Martyn China Clay Museum collection.

Early Dimson Brickworks
Grid Reference SX426717
The 1839 Calstock tithe map has a field near Dimson named Brick Kiln, with an adjoining field called Clay Field. Two adjoining circles, one in each field, could represent beehive kilns, while sheds marked on Brick Kiln field may have housed the brick preparation facilities. The land concerned was tenanted by members of the Bowhay family and in an 1856 Kelly's Trade Directory, Joseph Bowhay is listed as a brick maker and farmer at Dimson. By 1873 Joseph Bowhay had given up brick making. The 1883 O.S. map shows a clay pit but no kilns or sheds as indicated on the earlier tithe map. This appears to be a pioneering brick making operation superseded by other works. It is quite likely that their bricks were not marked.

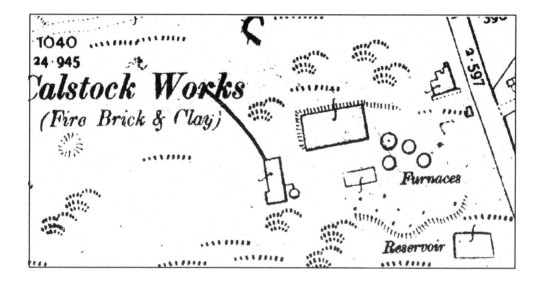

The works of the Calstock Fire Brick Co.© Crown Copyright 1907

Calstock Fire Brick Co. - Hingston Down
Grid Reference SX412715
The Calstock works, started by Thomas Westlake, commenced operations c.1860 and was acquired by the West of England Fireclay, Bitumen and Chymical (sic) Co. Ltd. in 1871. The chimney situated on Hingston Down, to the west of the works, was connected to four beehive kilns as seen on the map. One kiln which had been reported to have survived, now seems to have been demolished.
The principal products were coarse earthenware pots and cloam ovens [6]. White firebricks with no frog, were also manufactured.

Brickmark: CALSTOCK

Calstock Town Brickworks
Grid Reference SX432688
The works here may have been derived from other 'fictile' workings. Pococke in "Travels Through England" refers to a pottery in Calstock town in 1750 where they made coarse earthenware and earthenware (cloam) ovens [7]. The Borlase Letter Books held in the Morab Library, Penzance record in 1755 that 'we have a very fine white clay about 3 miles from us that was used in the pottery manufacture intended to have been carried on at Calstock but that scheme failed there'. Three miles distance from Calstock town would include the decomposed elvan quarried at Greenhill. The Sherborne Mercury (10 Oct. 1781) tells of a building 'to be let in Calstock: very commodious building for carrying on the manufacture of coarse earthenware or bricks: trial made by experienced potter who now makes crucibles' [8]. It appears this later became a brickworks. By 1856 the Calstock works were listed in Kelly's Directory as run by a brick maker John Westlake. The Westlake family controlled the works until the first World War using raw material from Greenhill [9]. By 1955 the works were converted into a 'chip' fruit basket manufactory. This lasted until 1963 when the site was sold for housing. A wall on the site contains some lumps of vitrified kiln lining from the two beehive kilns which the 1907 O.S. map suggests were employed here.

Brickmark: probably Westlake

3.2 South East Cornwall

Foss Brick and Tile Works, Millbrook
Grid Reference SX432523
Founded c.1870 this brick and tile works was ran by the Devonshire Brick Co. Ltd., until it closed in 1913 [10].
Mid- Devonian slate was obtained from a quarry adjacent to the works, from which bricks and terracotta household goods were manufactured. The bricks were red in colour with a frog.
The chimney used to service the kilns was reputed to be 160 feet (48.8 m.) in height. The site has now been totally cleared.

Brickmark: SWB

Pottery Brickworks - Insworke near Millbrook
Grid Reference SX424527
This brick works started c.1880 and operated under the ownership of the Devonshire Brick Co. until 1914. Thereafter it was run by Western Counties Brick Co. Ltd. (later Westbrick Products Ltd.), until closure c.1935.
The raw material for brick making, a mid-Devonian slate, was quarried behind the works and carried to the plant by railway. Like the Foss works, both brick and terracotta

household goods were manufactured. The Devonshire Brick Co. connected this works to the Foss Brickworks by a short railway. The chimney is recorded as being 164 feet (50 metres) high.

The brick colour was most likely to have been red.

The cleared site is now occupied by the Liberal Hall [11] and an overgrown area.

Brickmark: DEVONSHIRE/BRICK COMPANY/MILLBROOK

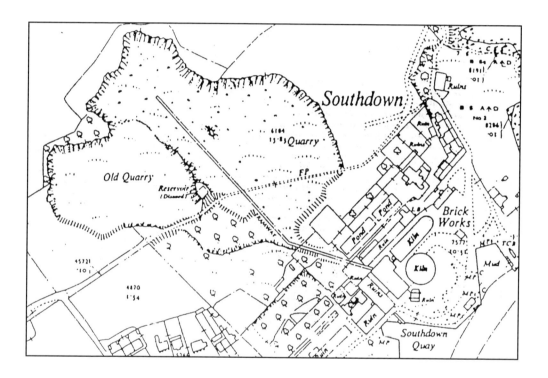

Southdown Brickworks © Crown Copyright 1907

Southdown Brickworks, Southdown, adjacent to quay

Grid Reference SX427527

Started in 1888 and operated by the South Down Metal, Chemical and Brick Co., it later became a separate company known as the Southdown Brick Co. In 1914 it amalgamated with other brick works in the area forming the Western Counties Brick Co. Ltd. to be taken over in 1928 by Westbrick Products Ltd. Although the remains on the site as well as published records suggest that there were 3 chimney-stacks, only 2 kilns are known with any certainty. These were a circular Hoffman Kiln connected to a rectangular chimney and a rectangular intermittent kiln with a circular chimney. As with the other brickworks in the area, ground-up Mid-Devonian Slates provided the raw material for brick manufacture. The bricks were red in colour with no frog. Although the works closed in 1942, they were opened briefly during the period 1946 to 1948 and there are records of a second reworking starting June 1954. Final closure was in 1956, as the works were no longer viable, due to increasing quantities of lime in the slate which caused deterioration in the quality of the bricks being produced. The chimneys, which had become unsafe, were demolished in 1972 along with some of the adjoining buildings. The site has now been completely cleared [12].

Brickmark: SDB

More East Cornwall Brickmarks. Wheal Martyn China Clay Museum collection.
Top Left: *SDB (Southdown)* Top Right: *Westbrick (Southdown)*
Bottom Left: *SWB (Foss)*
Bottom Right: *Launceston (Dutson Brickworks).*

Sheviock
Grid Reference SX370551
This 19th century brickworks was probably started in 1860 and in 1862 Kelly's Directory records the owners as Harvey & Roache, sadly it has proved difficult to pinpoint the site of their works. It may be that the works were sited somewhere near Hay Farm (SX374549), where there is a field known as "Brick Field", which may been the source of the clay. There is no other information at present.

Brickmark: not known

Torpoint
Grid Reference: Exact location unknown
Possible brick works at Kiln Point near Borough Grove. The 1851 census for Torpoint records Edward Clark, brick maker.

3.3 North Cornwall

Dutson Brickworks, Western Counties Brick Co. Ltd. - Lower Dutson Farm, near Launceston
Grid Reference SX345863
Following the discovery of good brick making clay of Eocene age, a brickworks was started on Lower Dutson Farm in the 1920's by an independent company, the Western Counties Brick Co. Ltd., who rented the land for the works and clay pit from the farm owner. All that remains is the water filled clay pit, which is now enjoyed by anglers [13]. The bricks were burnt in two beehive kilns, served by a single chimney 105 feet (32 metres) high. This chimney was demolished c.1950.

The bricks show evidence that the raw materials were not well mixed, probably because there was no pug mill at the works. The colour is variable depending on whereabouts in the kiln they were fired, but in general they are of an orange/yellow colour. These bricks were extensively used for building in Launceston, but as the rate of building decreased during the slump of the late 1920's and 30's, the works became uneconomical and closed sometime after 1930, so that the firm could concentrate on their Whitstone Brickworks.

Brickmark: LAUNCESTON

Whitstone Brick & Tile Co. Ltd., Bridgrule, Holsworthy on the border of Devon and Cornwall near the site of the former L.S.W.R. Whitstone and Bridgrule railway station.
Grid Reference: SS263015 (approx.)
Although originally in Cornwall, this site is now in Devon.

There have been brickworks on this site since at least 1898 when it was owned by Squire Glubb. Sometime later it passed to a Mr. Morris who was bought out in 1910 by the Western Counties Brick Co., who operated the works under the name of the Whitstone Brick and Tile Co. Ltd.

The pug mill and other machinery were driven initially by steam and later, by electric power. The bricks were wire cut and selected bricks were put into a hand press, which stamped the frog and the company's brick mark. In the mid-1950's the works was producing about 4,000,000 bricks per annum. The bricks were fired in either a beehive kiln or a nine-chamber tunnel kiln which were connected to a 120 foot (36.6 metres) chimney-stack.

The clay pit eventually covered about 12 acres (4.8 ha) and the raw material, interbedded shale and sandstone over lain by Head, was quarried by drag line. The harder sandstone which was not required was sorted by hand and rejected.

The works closed for brick production in August 1965. The site of the works has been cleared and is now the caravan park "Headley Wood" (after the first caravan site owners). The clay pit was used for clay pigeon shooting for a time.

Brickmark: WHITSTONE BRICK & TILE CO

Red Post near Launcells
Grid Reference: SS200000
Although recorded as being in operation in 1873 as the Launcells Brick & Tile Co., the works must have had a much longer history. It is thought that many Red Post bricks were used in the construction of the Bude Canal built 1819-25. In addition, the Burmsdon Aqueduct (SS280068) over the River Tamar, built between 1821 and 1823, is reputed to be built from brick burnt at Red Post. Edward Rudland took over the Launcells Brick & Tile Co., in 1880.

The brickworks, near Tyleyard Farm, were situated on the banks of the Bude Canal at the junction of the Holsworthy and Launceston branches. Although the main product was brick, other products which were made included pipes, tiles and chimney pots, all of which were made from a locally obtained clay soil [14].
Brickmark: the bricks were stamped with a simple mark using nails in a board . This type of marking is sometimes seen in other parts of England.

A Red Post brick showing the characteristic five nail brickmark.
Wheal Martyn China Clay Museum collection.

Delabole
Grid Reference SX075035
Research by Catherine Lorrigan on the Delabole Slate industry, has shown that in 1899 debris from the quarry was sent for testing with a view to using it for brick making. The bricks made using the waste were of good quality but in 1900 the project was abandoned as it was thought that the profit margin would be too small.

END NOTES

1   Booker F. 1967 The Industrial Archaeology of the Tamar Valley. David & Charles, Newton Abbot
2   Nicholls B. 1972 The Tamar Firebrick and Clay Company. Industrial Archaeology, Vol. 9, No. 3, pp.242 – 264 David & Charles, Newton Abbot
3   "Life in Cornwall in the Late 19th. Century" 1972. Ed. Rita Barton. D. B. Barton Ltd., Truro, Cornwall
4   Children's Employment Commission 4th and 5th Reports. 1865 - 1866. Appendix to the 5th Report, p.48 (Copies in the Morrab Library, Penzance.)
5   Paige R.T. 1982, "The Tamar Valley at Work"
6   A roughly hemispherical shaped hollow clay structure, with a small access door at the front. Used for baking bread.
7   Pococke, R. "Travels Through England 1750 Reprinted in "Early Tours in Devon & Cornwall" 1968, p.204, David & Charles, Newton Abbot
8   Sherborne Mercury 10th October 1781
9   Calstock Archive Notes compiled by Roger Massey, 2003
10 Elworthy J. 1994 "Millbrook Brick By Brick". E .J. Richard Ltd., Plymouth
11 Carne T. 1985 "Cornwall's Forgotten Corner". Lodenek Press. p.107
12 Ibid. p.111
13 See Murphy J. S. Alternative Farm – From bricks to fish. North Cornwall Advertiser, November 1990.
14 See Rendell J. 1979 "Along The Bude Canal" p.36
15 Ibid. p.52

CHAPTER 4

BRICK MAKING SITES - CENTRAL CORNWALL

4.1 Newquay Area

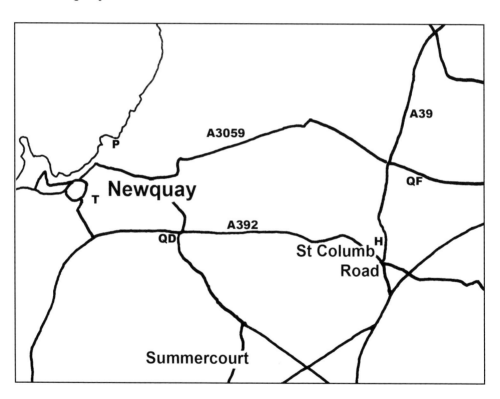

Sketch map of the Newquay area showing the approximate locations of the recorded brickworks mentioned in the text. Not to scale.

H - Halloon   P - Porth   QD - Quintrell Downs
QF - Quoit Farm   T - Tolcarne

St. Columb Road
Grid Reference SW911595
Situated on the edge of the St. Austell china clay area, the works were owned at some time by Mostyn and Bennett, who also had interests in other brickworks nearby. The three circular downdraught kilns at St. Columb were built by Stephen Sharp whose family had experience of brick making in Newton Abbot. A lease of 1884 for brick making here shows 2 acres of ground to the east side of the main road, with an adit. In 1893 the works were known as the North Cornwall Brick Co. The works complete with all equipment and buildings was offered for sale in September 1899 **[1]**. As can be seen on the map they were south of St. Columb Road railway station, with the clay pits to the east, on both sides of the railway line. The southermost of these was connected to the works by the adit.

Kelly's Directory for 1887 records the North Cornwall Brick & Tile Co. Ltd., which was located at Halloon near St. Columb Road (Grid Reference SW912598). On the 1907 Ed. Ordnance Survey Map, three small clay pits are marked, all of which have now been in filled. The clay pits were still in work in 1897 when some clay was carried by horse and cart to the brickworks at St. Columb Road.

Brickmarks: NB/ST COLUMB

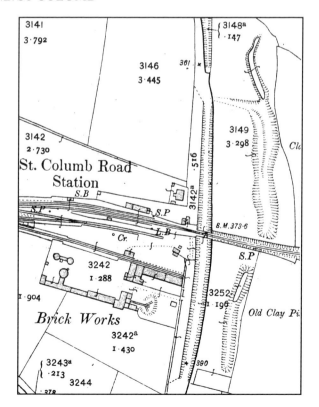

St. Columb Road Brickworks and clay pits. © *Crown Copyright 1907*

Brickmarks used by North Coast brickworks. Note that these are poorly impressed. Left: PORTH *Right:* NB/TOLCARNE (Newquay Brickworks).

Quintrell Downs, near St. Columb Major
Grid Reference SW852604
It is not known who operated these brickworks, although it is suggested that it was one of the Newquay brick making companies. The clay source was a decomposed elvan dyke (probably the same dyke as at Porth, Newquay) [2]. The clay pit and the base of two beehive kilns were visible in the mid 20th century close to the Par – Newquay branch railway line. The kilns were also marked on the 1962, 2½ inch (1:25,000) Ordnance Survey map.
Brick colour, red.

Brickmark: not known

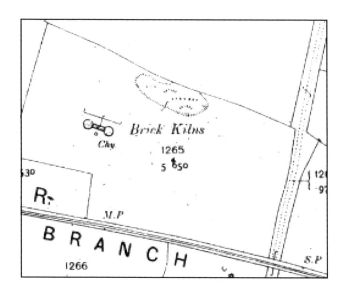

Location map for Quintrell Downs © *Crown Copyright 1907*

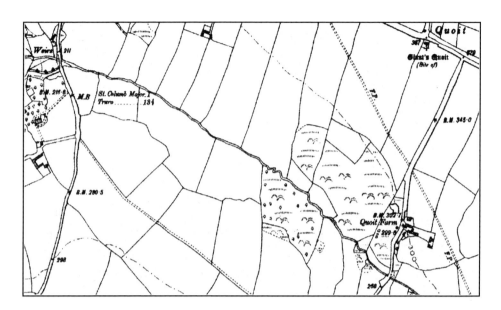

Location map for Quoit Farm © Crown Copyright 1990

Quoit Farm, near Quintrell Downs
Grid Reference SW922613
It is suggested by local residents that there were brickworks to the west of Quoit Farm, with clay pits to the east. At the farm there are some buildings constructed from soft, rather crudely made yellow brick, which may have been made here. At Ruthvoes nearby to the south, inspection of a chapel under reconstruction (2003), has shown that similar bricks had been used in part of the structure.

Brickmark: not known

Tolcarne Brickworks, Newquay - below railway viaduct
Grid Reference SW818614
This brickworks had a short life and by 1896, the works and brick making equipment was advertised for sale by auction (see Chapter 2, p.38). According to the sale notice, the lease had 15 years to run, which suggests that brick making had commenced in 1886. The extensive list of equipment listed includes a brick-making machine capable of 10,000 bricks per day. The early closure suggests that it may have been badly judged.

The source of the raw material was mud from the bed of the River Gannel, giving rise to bricks of a medium red colour. The site of the works is now a tennis court built in the gardens adjoining Edgcumbe Avenue. Almost beneath the viaduct is a seat made from Tolcarne bricks, during the 1930's when the gardens were laid out.

Brickmarks: NB/TOLCARNE

Seat constructed from Tolcarne bricks in the gardens on the west side of Edgcumbe Avenue, Newqauy.

Porth, Newquay - at the eastern end of Porth Beach
Grid Reference SW832629
From 1880 this brickworks was owned by Martyn & Bennett [3] and may have changed hands c.1909 when John Argall took over. Clay was obtained 'from a decomposed elvan lode (see earlier - Quintrell Downs) and the bricks were a light medium red colour, with a frog. The site was cleared and is now a Caravan Park.

Brickmarks: PORTH and NPC
Lettering: 1¾ inches (NPC)

Padstow - St. George's Well, Camel Estuary
Grid Reference SW919765
A photograph published [4] of the St. George's Well area taken before 1914, shows what appears to have been brickworks possibly in the late 19th or early 20th century.

Brickmark: unknown

Wadebridge, east side of River Camel
Grid Reference SW990728
In the 1930's there were the remains of brickworks at William Martyn's Quay near Bradford Quay. It was probably owned and run by William Martyn. It is said that a local landowner who lived nearby did not allow the kiln to be fired if the wind would blow smoke in his direction!

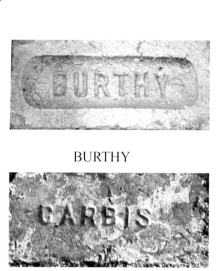

BURTHY

INDIAN QUEEN (Gaverigan)

CARBIS

LISKEARD (Carkeet)

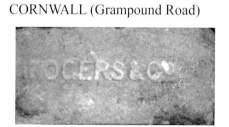

CORNWALL (Grampound Road)

PAR

ROGERS & Co. (Wheal Remfry)

JR & Co. (Wheal Remfry)

CARLOGGAS

ENGLISH CHINA CLAY SALES (Carloggas)

Some Brickmarks used by Central Cornwall works.

4.2 The St. Austell China Clay Area

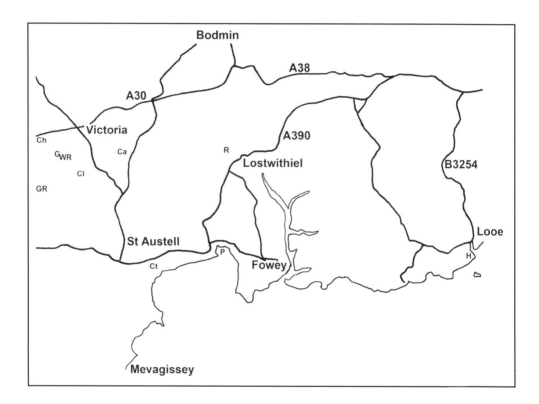

Sketch map of the Central Cornwall area showing the approximate locations of some of the brickworks in the area. Not to scale.

Ca - Carbis Cl - Carloggas Ct - Charlestown
G - Gaverigan GR - Grampound Road H - Hannafore (Looe)
P - Par R - Redmoor WR - Wheal Remfry

In 1546 Georgius Agricola [5] noted that 'Amongst the men who work with clay are those who make bricks.' As far as china clay was concerned the first brickworks of any size was set up on Lee Moor in Devon in the 1840's, to be followed by many others in the St. Austell china clay area.

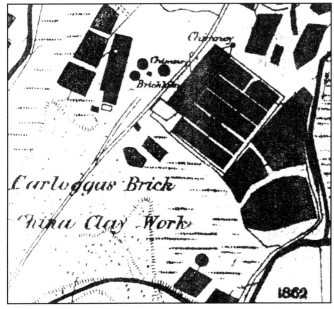

Left:
*Carloggas Brickworks
adjacent to china clay
tanks and dry.*
© *Crown Copyright 1880*

Below:
*Map of Carbis Brick-
works showing the clay
pit (bottom left) and
tramway.*
© *Crown Copyright 1907*

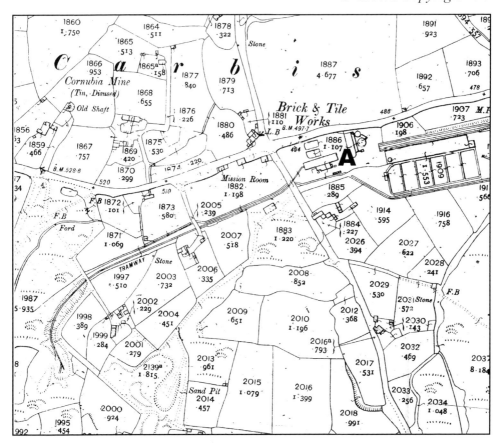

Carloggas near Nanpean. May be referred to as Barakellis
Grid Reference SW958551
Situated close to the site where Cookworthy found china clay. A lease was taken out in October 1856 and a brickworks started c.1860. By 1869 it was being managed by Edward Stocker of the West of England Co. [6]. Ownership passed to English China Clays around 1919, when it is thought the brick mark was changed from WECO to ECCS (English China Clay Sales) and perhaps in 1932 to CARLOGGAS. The 1880 O.S. map indicates that there were three beehive kilns, connected to a single chimney in operation at the works. The cleared site was close to the No 7 Buell dryer site at Drinnick, near Nanpean.

The bricks are buff coloured with no frog.

Brickmarks: CARLOGGAS, ECCS, WECO

Carbis [7], south of road from Bugle to Roche
Grid Reference SX001596
Brick making was started here by Absalom Hancock of Roche in 1883, when he built a circular Scrivener Kiln using bricks purchased from Lee Moor, Devon. In 1892 the works was bought by David Cock, also of Roche. Soon after this (c.1894), a second kiln was in operation. By May 1917 the brickworks had changed hands once more and a limited company trading as the Carbis China Clay & Brick Co. Ltd. was registered c.1920. In 1929 this company was sold and acquired by English China Clays.

Between 1919 and 1924 two more Scrivener Kilns were built, giving four operational kilns connected to a single chimney. Only one kiln was fired at a time, so that while it was being fired, there was one loading, one unloading, while the fourth could be serviced as necessary. The brick making material was contaminated china-clay, obtained from Carbis Common, and transported to the works by a light tram-road (diagonally across map). A 12 ft. 8 inch (3.86 metre) diameter and 4 ft. (1.22 metre) breast, overshot water-wheel (just below A on map), provided the power to drive a single pug mill (photograph, p. 40), through a train of gears connected by a belt drive to the water-wheel the remains of which can still be found adjacent to the surviving kilns. The bricks were hand moulded and partly dried in a drying shed for c.24 hours, after which they were pressed and stamped with the company's brickmark. The source of heat for the drying shed was a furnace, connected to it by flues. During its lifetime Carbis brickworks produced building bricks, fire bricks, tiles, special bricks for Cornish ranges, as well as kiln (clay dry) tiles for the china-clay industry. Another speciality was the manufacture of fireplaces using bricks or briquettes. During the 1930's it became cheaper to import building bricks from S. Wales and as a consequence of this, and after a kiln collapsed while in use on 2nd January 1942, the works closed permanently.

The bricks were a creamy white colour, no frog, size: 9 inches x 4 ¼ inches x 2 ¼ inches.

Brickmark: CARBIS

Surviving structures at Carbis Brickworks.
Left: *Square chimney stack.*
Below: *One of several surviving brick kilns. Note the edge of the chimney at the right hand side of the photograph.*
As a result of a housing development at the nearby china-clay dry, some of the kilns and chimney on this site will be consolidated and preserved.

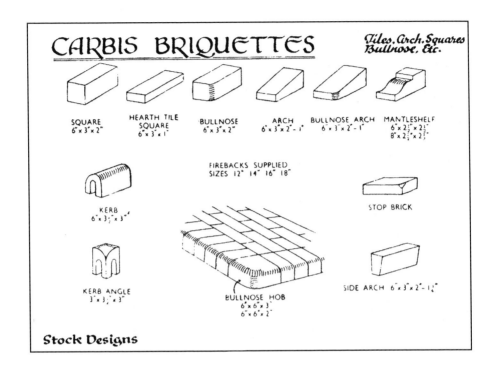

Advertisements for Carbis building products available for the home in the 1930's
Top: *Speciality briquettes.*
Bottom: *Illustration of a fireplace taken from a Carbis Advertisement. A painted 'Sunburn' Carbis fireplace (slightly different design to the above), may be seen at the Britannia Inn near Par. It is also thought that fireplaces similar to this were supplied to the Great Western Railway for use in their waiting rooms.*

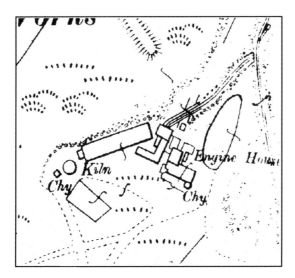

Burthy Brickworks © Crown Copyright 1907

Burthy, east of Summercourt
Grid Reference SW919557
Negative evidence from the earliest Ordnance Survey map suggests that this brickworks
started soon after 1880. In 1887 the works were operated by T. Nicholls & Co. The power
to drive the brick making machinery was taken from a rotative beam engine. The Burthy
works produced creamy-pink coloured building bricks with or without a frog, firebricks
and kiln (clay dry) tiles.

The site was destroyed during china-clay working of Melbur pit.

Brickmarks: BURTHY (with frog); T. NICHOLLS & C° ; N & Co. / ST ENODER;
T NICHOLLS & CO/ST ENODER (no frog)

Advertisement for Burthy clay and bricks

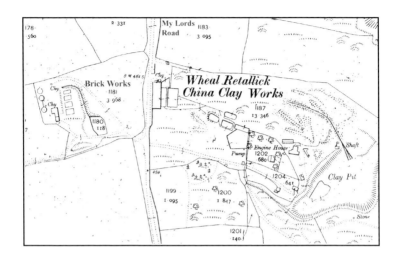

Chytane Brickworks © Crown Copyright 1907

Chytane, My Lords Road
Grid Reference SW913561
Started c.1875, the brickworks was to the west of Wheal Retallick china-clay works.
The source of the clay was a decomposed elvan obtained from a pit on the opposite side
of My Lords Road and the two were connected by a level running under the roadway.
Other than bricks, recorded products include 6 inch (15 cms.) square floor tiles as well as
coping and blue vitrified bricks with matching gutters for stabling [8]. Although the site
of the works has been cleared, the footprint of the kiln was visible on aerial photographs
until the 1960's.

Brickmark: CHYTANE (faintly marked)

Wheal Remfry Brick & Tile Works, ½ mile N of Retew
Grid Reference: SW929577
Operational from the last decade of the 19th century, this was the last Cornish brickworks
open, not closing until 1972. The works was operated by J. Rogers & Co. until 1921,
being succeeded by H. D. Pochin, by 1933 it was a subsidiary of English China Clays
Lovering Pochin & Co. Ltd. and known as the Wheal Remfry Brick and Tile Works.

The works was set up here to take advantage of water power which was used to drive
a pan grinder. The first kiln built here by Stephen Sharp was a Newcastle kiln but this
was not satisfactory and did not produce sufficient heat. This was later converted to two
downdraught kilns known as Nos. 3 and 4. Nos. 1 and 2 were beehive kilns with shallow
crowns, built later.

The works used a variety of clays including decomposed elvan, china clay which had

THE LAST BRICK MAKERS IN CORNWALL

Photograph of the work force at Wheal Remfry taken on the retirement of Tom May in October 1958. This photograph, taken by Roy Dutch, originally appeared in the E.E.C. Review, Christmas 1958 . The print from which this was copied was supplied by John Osborne. Note the beehive kiln behind the group.
Back Row (L-R): *Les May, Godfrey Jasper, Sam Billing, Owen Warne. Ivor Hooper, John Osborne.* ***Middle Row (L-R):*** *Syd Hancock (fitter), Stafford Luke, Percy Common (fitter), Derek May, Frank Williams, Bill Beare, Tommy Chamberlin, Joe Barker, Harold Roberts, Fred Brewer (fitter), Phill Billing, Tony Brewer.* ***Front Row (l-R):*** *Don Sharp (Captain), Alf Common, Arch Common, Tom May, Ford Knight, Cliff Sharp (Captain).*

failed to meet potter's requirements, sweepings from dries and occasionally a clay mud dredged from the Par River.

The main product of the works was porous tiles for pan kilns. Also made were shaped tiles, firebricks and two types of building brick. Bricks are a white or cream colour and variable in length ranging from 8 ½ to 9 inches (21.6 to 22.9 cms.). Examples of their firebricks are to be found in the fireboxes of many clay dries and in West Cornwall, in the lining of Brunton Calciners and their associated flues.

Brickmarks: ROGERS & C°, ROGERS, JR & CO, ECLP

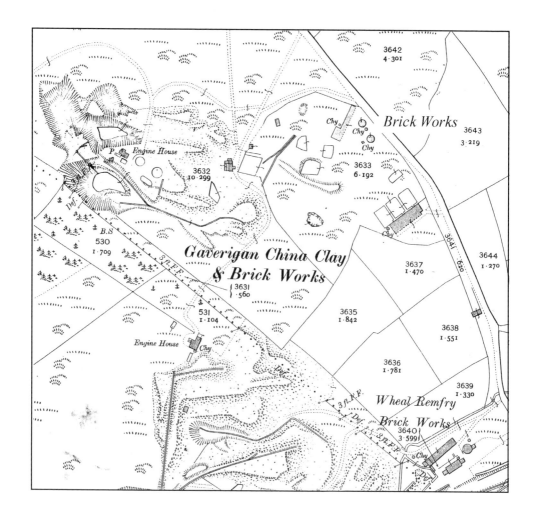

Gaverigan and Wheal Remfry Brickworks
© Crown Copyright 1907

Gaverigan, situated north Wheal Remfry Brickworks
Grid Reference: SW928581
This brickworks opened c.1890 and was known as the Indian Queens Brick Co. Two beehive kilns were built here by Stephen Sharp who had built kilns at St. Columb Road. He used St. Columb bricks in their construction and later supplied bricks for kilns at Wheal Remfry. Between 1897 and 1902 the works changed hands and was known as Scantlebury & Co. In 1906 Richard Lewis took over, followed some time later by Tapley & Payne. In the 1980's an underground chamber where the brick makers mined the elvan clay used was found, but the site has now been filled for safety reasons.

Brickmarks: IQBC, INDIAN QUEEN, S&CO

GRAMPOUND ROAD TILE

CHYTANE TILE

GRAMPOUND ROAD

GRAMPOUND ROAD

GPD (Grampound Road)

CLARK (Charlestown)

LOOE

T. NICHOLLS & Co (Burthey)

Top Row: *Floor tile makers marks from Central Cornwall works. The Grampound Road tile is 9 inches x 8 ¾ inches and between 1¼ inches and 1½ inches thick. That from Chytane is 6 inches square.*
Remainder: *Further brickmarks from Central Cornwall*

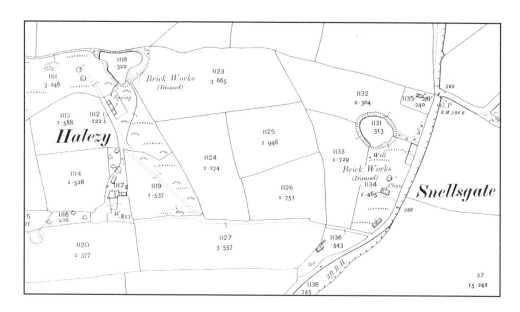

The brickworks of the Grampound Road Brick & Tile Co.
© Crown Copyright 1907

Grampound Road Brick & Tile Company – sites at Halezy and Snellsgate
Grid Reference Halezy: SW916512; Snellsgate: SW920514
There are two small brick making sites, about ½ mile north of Grampound Road which are marked on the 1910 edition Ordnance Survey map, as "disused". Whilst they may represent two independent works it seems likely that for at least part of their life, one company was involved. The Grampound Road Brick & Tile Company Ltd. with offices at Lemon Quay, Truro, is listed in Kelly's 1883 Directory. Bricks can be found with this title in full or abbreviated as GPD. The 1889 edition of the directory has reference to Cornwall (The) Brick Tile and Terra Cotta Co. Ltd. with James and Company as managers and offices at Grampound Road. It is possible that the James concerned is J. Harris-James a local person who was involved with various mining projects. This may represent a take over of the Grampound Road Brick & Tile Company.

It seems likely that the clay was dug from nearby pits at Halezy and Snellsgate, was an alluvial Head deposit of pebbly loam, some 5 - 15 feet (1½ - 4½ metres) thick.

Work commenced around 1880 and by 1887 the company employed a consultant, Robert Scattergood, a blue brick specialist, who later (1889) took them to court over underpayment of fees to the tune of £80.

In 1889 [9] C.B. T. & T.C. Co. were advertising the sale of "Red facing bricks and Plain Pressed Vitrified Blue bricks for foundations, sewage works & c."

The remains of a beehive kiln and pond survive on private premises at Halezy and a brick-built cottage on corner of the main road and the road leading to the kilns (right hand corner of map), may have been the work's managers home or office. There are no remains at Snellsgate.

Brick colour red and blue, typically with a frog. Measured size 8 ¾ inches x 4 inches x 3 inches

Brick marks: GPD; CORNWALL; G-P^D-R^D/ B & T C^O L^{TD}; CORNWALL/ B.T&T.C^O/ GRAMPOUND ROAD

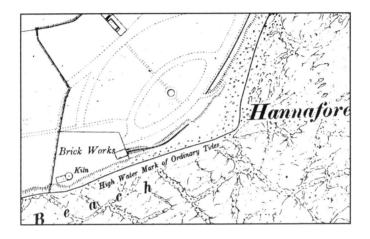

Hannafore Brickworks, West Looe © Crown Copyright 1907

Hannafore Brick Works, Hannafore Point, West Looe
Grid Reference SX255523
Hannafore brickworks were started c.1893 by Joseph Thomas, the civil engineer in charge of the Hannafore West Estate development. Thomas died in 1901 and the works was taken over by John Alderman who continued operation until closure in 1910. John Alderman is reputed to have ran Par brickworks in the 1840's, so if this is true, he must have been a very old man! The raw material was Head, a pale yellow-brown coloured loam with small stones, which outcrops in the low cliffs at Hannafore Point. The map indicates that there was one beehive kiln. The bricks were red in colour and a little oversized [10]. It was boasted that they were the best bricks made in Cornwall.

The bricks were used for Hannafore West Estate, although many were shipped from Wallace Quay, Hannafore to local towns such as Downderry. A bowling green now occupies the brickworks site.

Brickmark: LOOE

View of Par Harbour in the late 19th century. In the foreground, is a barge which was used to bring raw material from the harbour area to the brickworks.

Par Harbour [11] (see jacket photograph)
Grid Reference SX076532
Brick making started at Par in 1836 and, after several unsuccessful attempts to make brick from local mud, Messrs. Treffry, Clunes & Co. advertised for the services of an "expert brick-maker". In 1844 John Alderman, locally known as Bricky Jack, took on the job and was soon able to sort out the problems. Clay and sand which were largely china clay residues washed down the rivers, were dug at low tide and loaded into barges for transportation to the brickworks. The ratio used was two parts mud and one part sand. The bricks were burnt in a beehive kiln. Bricks were used for the tall lead smelter chimney here which was nearly 300 feet (91.5 metres) high and now demolished.

By April 1928 the equipment at Par was advertised for sale, including a brick-making machine capable of producing 8,000 bricks per day. The works closed and the site was cleared in 1935.

Brick colour red to pink, with frog. Typical size 8 ¾ inches x 4 ½ inches x 2 ¼ inches

Brickmark: PAR

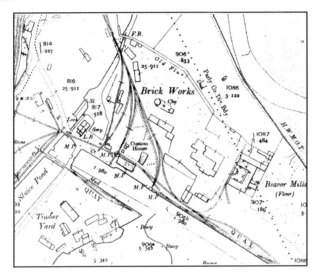

Par Harbour Brickworks © Crown Copyright 1907

Par Station Brickworks
Grid Reference: SX077541 (approx.)
In 1862 a lease on three parcels of land near Par Station was agreed between J. Frances Basset of Tehidy and John Stibbs Bush, brick-maker of Lostwithiel. A brick works and stock of bricks was advertised for sale in the Royal Cornwall Gazette 4th December 1863, recorded as being near Par Station. This short lived brickworks was too early to be marked on the Ordnance Survey maps.

Brickmark: Not known

Par, Pembroke Mine
Grid Reference SX058526
A possible brickworks at Pembroke Mine [12] is referred to in the Royal Cornwall Gazette dated March 1st 1878, where it is reported that brick making from china clay is "about to be commenced near the site of the now abandoned Pembroke Mines". A secondary tin recovery plant was sited here shown on the 1880 O.S. map and replaced by a clay work recovering 'mica' clay from the nearby river shown on the 1907 O.S. map. This could be the source of the clay mentioned. Bricks do not appear to have been made here.

Charlestown, **Brick Hill,** Duporth Road.

Brick making probably started in 1795 mainly through the efforts of Charles Rashleigh, founder of Charlestown. Brick making using local clay from 1795 is noted by Hitchens and Drew, p. 51 **[13]**. The name Brick Lane which appears in the 1861 census returns and now known locally as Brick Hill rather than the official name of Duporth Road, may commemorate the brickworks which is thought to have been on the road to Rashleigh's country House at Duporth. These bricks were used for the inner skin of the house (outer was Pentewan Stone). Brick colour red with no frog.

Brickmark: Probably not marked

Charlestown, Charlestown Road

A second brickworks at Charlestown is identified by a lease of 1854 which refers to a kiln near the Higher Pond at Charlestown. Here Edward Clark and his son William were allowed to take clay from the pond to make 'bricks, tiles and drainpipes'. The clay was derived from 'contamination' in the five mile leat taking water to Charlestown for use in the harbour. Some bricks and drying kiln tiles have been found here, but it is thought that the works was short lived. Brick colour buff .

Brickmark: CLARK

Pentewan

References which suggest that bricks were manufactured in Pentewan are probably incorrect and stem from the name of a firm set up to produce concrete blocks, using local sand. The firm, started in 1907, was originally known as the Pentewan Brick and Stone Co., which by 1908 had changed to Pentewan Development and Brick Co. Ltd. These names may have reflected an intention to make bricks. However a further emendation came in 1909, when it was renamed (perhaps more correctly) as the Pentewan Block and Development Co. Ltd. Concrete blocks marked 'Pentewan' are known.

Carkeet, Draynes Valley (R. Fowey), near Liskeard. Off the Bolventnor to Redgate road.

Grid Reference SX218732

Here a partly kaolinised granite, which was discovered in an unsuccessful china clay works trial, was used as the source material for brick and terracotta manufacture. The brickworks, which is only marked on the 1906 edition Ordnance Survey Map, was started in either 1885 or 1886. The operation which was known as The Terra Cotta & China Clay Co. **[14]**, only lasted about a decade, as it was found not to pay **[15]** probably due in part to its isolated position and poor access to a market for the products.

The description below is based on a visit to the privately owned site in October 2003: There is a square sectioned chimney stack and the remains of four buildings on the site, two of the buildings appear to be used by the local farmer to house animals.

The bricks used to construct the chimney are buff in colour with diamond lozenge patterns in glazed brown brick. They are imported and are marked "RAMSAY". This is the brick mark of a firm which operated at Derwenthaugh in the Tyne valley, making firebrick. The 25 foot (7.6 metres) chimney is connected to a beehive kiln with an internal diameter of 12 feet (3.7 metres), with nine fire holes and a north facing wicket.

A building just to the north of this kiln appears to be a drying shed which had a separate section at the north end which probably housed a pug mill which was driven by a water wheel. The pug mill and water wheel are not extant, although the wheel pit outside the north wall can still be seen. This section of the shed was probably also used for moulding. There are six fire holes along the west side to provide heat for drying (Chapter 2 p.41).

At right angles to the drying shed is a large building whose original purpose is unknown but which is now used as a barn. At the back of this is a small Newcastle Kiln, which has been built into the natural slope of the ground and is now almost completely obscured. This kiln is very small with internal dimensions of 9 feet by 6 feet 6 inches (2.7 by 2 metres). There are three fire holes on the western end (nearest the barn). Internally the kiln is arched and the wicket, in the short side facing south. The chimney on the east side of the kiln and marked on the 1907 Ordnance Survey Map has been demolished. It may be that the bricks were reused to rebuild the end of the barn nearest the kiln.

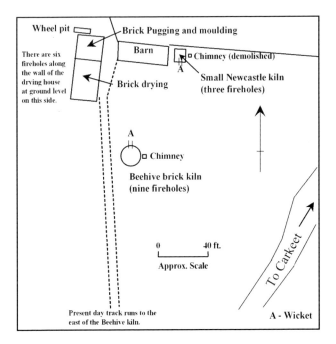

Carkeet Brickworks. Sketch map based on visit to the site in October 2003.

It has been recorded [16] that the works also produced decorative terracotta and at least one example can be seen on a house in Liskeard. We would suggest that the Newcastle Kiln was used to fire this terracotta.

As well as broken brick a red coloured ridge tile marked "Liskeard" was found on the site. Bricks made here were buff coloured with a frog.

Brickmark: LISKEARD

Carkeet Brickworks. General view of the area. The beehive kiln is in the vegetation to the left of the chimney which has a pronounced lean - one fire hole can just be seen to the right of the metal framed structure in the foreground.

W. H. LAKE & SON

Earthenware
Manufacturers
and Builder's
Merchants.

Sole Makers of the noted
CORNISH   POTTERY

ST. AUSTELL
AND
TRURO

Advertisement for Lake's Pottery in the 1930's.
The St. Austell premises were on the south side of East Hill.

4.3 THE TRURO AREA

Truro

There are several records of attempts at brick making to the south of the city at Newham on the Truro River. These were largely unsuccessful. At Newham, Francis Moult and partners built a smelting house, which included a brick-house (= Scotch kiln) in the early 18th century. Records indicate that in 1710 bricks and "Windsor Clay" was taken to Newham from Calenick [17]. In 1892 the brick-house and the associated crucible works was advertised for sale [18]. A number of other attempts at brick making are recorded, for example in the mid-19th century Messrs. Rowe erected a kiln near the Parade and baked a load of bricks made from river mud. These were far from satisfactory as they disintegrated when they became wet. Later, in 1877, Mr. W. Beesley Radford sought permission to make bricks, while in 1892 Messrs. Harvey's (of Hayle) built a temporary kiln at Lower Newham with the intention of using river mud [19]. The outcome of these last ventures is not recorded.

Lake's Pottery, Richmond Hill, Truro
Grid Reference SW818448 (approx.)
Situated on the south side of Richmond Hill (Chapel Hill), until its closure in 1970's was Lake's Pottery. The earliest extant records show that a pottery, which had existed on this site from at least the late 17th century, was leased by Lord Falmouth to Edward Dennis Tucket in 1845, being occupied subsequently by W. H. Lake (later W. H. Lake & Son Ltd.). This firm which was famed for its cloam ovens, is referred to in a number of books on domestic architecture [20]. The clay was originally obtained locally from a nearby field (the site is now occupied by Bosvigo School). Later raw material was brought from St. Agnes and from Fremington near Barnstaple. The original kiln was a simple open topped, stone built cylindrical structure which was modified in 1875 by adding a brick dome. This was replaced by a more modern coal fired kiln in 1943 which survived until the closure of the pottery [21].

The products of Truro pottery included items for farming, fishing and household use (see Chapter 7, later). Two important items were the bussa (a large container in which pilchards were salted) and the cloam oven (beehive shaped earthenware ovens used for baking bread - the last were produced here in 1935). Also manufactured were pitchers, baking bowls, wash bowls, salting pans, plant pots, rhubarb forcers and urinals. For the building trade they made ridge tiles, roof finials, chimney pots and chimney pot covers or louvres.

Calenick Crucible Manufactory
Grid Reference SW822431
William Cookworthy writing in 1768 referred to problems in obtaining suitable bricks for his pottery kiln. He tells of a crucible maker in Truro who made

bricks of 'a Moor stone clay found in that Neighbourhood'. These bricks were apparently 'sufficiently unvitrifiable' to form an arch to bear a coal fire immediately under it [22]. The crucible maker is thought to have been Jacob Lieberich who made crucibles for assaying purposes at Calenick near Truro, later succeeded by Mitchell. Crucibles were a major product at Calenick in the 18th and 19th centuries but these works also contributed to brick making in the County, before their closure in 1891.

The source of the clay used at Calenick is believed to be Killiganoon on the east side of Carnon Downs, where a decomposed elvan was worked [23]. The clay pits are marked as being 'old' on the 1880 Ordnance Survey Map and have since been infilled. The Calenick crucible works were about two miles from the pits.

Trelonk, near Ruan Lanihorne
Grid Reference SW886412
In 1891 a lease on land owned by Arthur Tremayne of Carclew was agreed with John Truscott Paul of Trelonk, Giles Williams of Ruan, Albertus Dingle of Fowey and J. M. Bennetts, for the purpose of making bricks from materials obtained from Trelonk. The works, operational between 1891 and 1907, was situated on the north side of Tuckingmill Creek. In 1897 the enterprise was known as the Trelonk Brick and China Clay Co. Ltd. with J. M. Bennetts as secretary. Bennetts was the only one of the original signatories to the lease who was associated with the works at its closure.

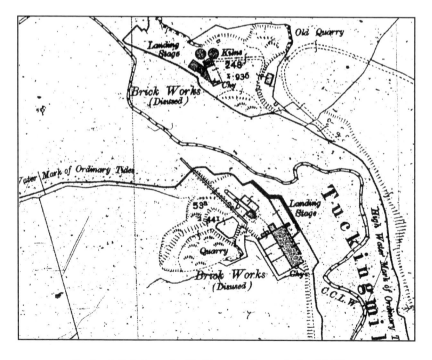

Trelonk Brickworks © Crown Copyright 1907

The brickworks consisted of two beehive kilns connected to a square chimney along with two hacks or drying sheds. The bricks, made from river mud and possibly material from a nearby quarry, were buff-orange in colour with a shaped frog (see below).

Brickmark: TRELONK

A china clay dry at Ardevora Veor, on the opposite bank which has been labelled as a brickworks by the Ordnance Survey, was leased by Lord Falmouth to Herbert Moore of Teignmouth, James Calvert of London and William Dow of Sussex in 1899, to wash and dry clay for the Fal River Clay Company. The works were let for 21 years, but in the event the licence was surrendered in 1906 [24]. It is thought that this was an attempt to recover lowgrade 'mica clay' from the river for use in coarse earthenware manufacture.

Above: *Trelonk brickworks.*
Note the kilns, middle left and the dry building middle right, both with chimneys. What appears to be piles of clay and coal can be seen lower right.
Left: *Brickmark.*

St. Agnes, *Trevaunance Cove Brickworks. The beehive kiln with a central chimney stack is in the centre of this picture which was taken c.1900. There are a number of postcards of this view from different angles, which always show the chimney as central .*

Trevaunance Cove Brickworks, near St. Agnes at the seaward end of the Trevaunance Valley
Grid Reference SW722517
Many late 19th century post cards show that there was a circular downdraught kiln with a central chimney, near the mineral processing plant at the foot of the Trevaunance Valley near St. Agnes. As can be seen it is on the landward side of the tin streaming plant, with the old Trevaunance Foundry (with the tall chimney), behind. The site shown in the photograph is now a public car park which is opposite the Driftwood Spars Hotel.

This type of beehive kiln, with a central chimney stack, is rare in Cornwall where all of the beehive kilns known to the authors have a separate stack, often connected to two or more kilns. The central chimney type of kiln was figured in a note in the British Clayworker [25] and is reproduced here (opposite). These kilns were never popular because of their heavy consumption of fuel.

Bricks here may have been made using the clay-like residues from the tin stream works (to left of and behind the kiln), or from nearby sand and clay deposits on St. Agnes Beacon **[26]**.

Brick Mark: Unknown

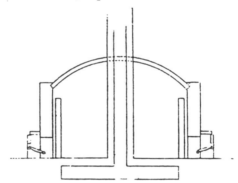

LETTERS TO A YOUNG BRICK-MAKER.—XV.

DEAR TOM,

Down-Draught Kiln, with stack in centre of kiln.—Another arrangement for circular down-draught kilns, in use in many parts of the United Kingdom is that in which the stack is built in the centre of the kiln, and projects through the centre of the dome or crown, as per sketch.

Circular Down-Draught Kiln, with Stack in Centre.

You will observe that the fire, after passing over the screen down through the goods and perforated bottom into the flue, is drawn through the stack in the middle of the kiln. The reason for the stack being so placed is that the heat generated in burning the goods, at the same time raises the stack to a very high temperature, thus creating a very quick draught artificially, and by this means ensuring a better colour of the goods. Very capital results are obtained in this direction by their use, but the consumption of fuel is very heavy.

Illustration of a beehive kiln with a central chimney stack [27].

END NOTES

1 The British Clayworker, Sept., 1899, p.190 (This journal was mainly concerned with brick making in Great Britain).

2 Geological Survey Sheet Memoir 346, 1906, p.53

3 Listed in "The Newquay Guardian and North Cornwall Advertiser" of 23 December 1887, as brick makers

4 Claude Berry 1976 "Padstow" Lodenek Press

5 Georgius Agricola 1546 "De Natura Fossilium." p.89

6 R. M. Barton 1966 "A History of the Cornish China-clay Industry." 212 pp., D. Bradford Barton, Truro

7 Information in this summary was taken mainly from: Tonkin J. 1997 Carbis Brickworks. Plymouth Minerals and Mining Club, Vol.26, No.3

8 Royal Cornwall Gazette, 24/01/1889, p.2

9 Royal Cornwall Gazette 24/01/1889, p.1

10 Letter from George Vaughan Ellis RIBA to J. Ferguson, 13 February 2002

11 Notes taken from: J. Penderill-Church August 1974, "Bricky Dick Looks Back" ECC Press

12 Trevithick Society Newsletter No. 29, May 1980, p.5

13 Hitchens F. and S. Drew 1824 "The History of Cornwall" Vol. 2, p.51 Helston

14 W. H. H. Huddy letter to The Cornish Times, Friday, 13th March 1959.

15 Trevithick Society Newsletter No.10, August 1975, pp.12 & 13 and No.12, February 1976, p.11

16 W. H. H. Huddy, *ibid.*

17 Douch, H. L. 1977 "The Book of Truro' p.44

18 *Ibid.* p.44

19 *Ibid.* p.32

20 For example: Barley M. W. 1961 The English Farmhouse and Cottage. Routledge, Kegan Paul Ltd., London. 1987 Edition, Paper Back, 297pp. p. 167-68

21 Brears P. C. D. 1972 Techniques of the Truro Pottery. Folk Life No. 10, pp.47-54

22 Letter from Will. Cookworthy to Thos. Pitt. September 1768. CRO Ref. DDF(4) 80

23 de la Beche, Sir Henry. 1839 The Geology of Cornwall, Devon and West Somerset. London, p.177

24 Letter from Lord Falmouth to Charles Thurlow, October 1996

25 British Clayworker, January 1894

26 Clay from deposits on St. Agnes Beacon is known to have been favoured by miners for attaching candles to their hats when working underground. This clay was also used by Lake's Pottery **(see p.92)**.

27 British Clayworker, January 1894

CHAPTER 5

BRICK MAKING SITES - WEST CORNWALL

5.1 Around the Fal Estuary

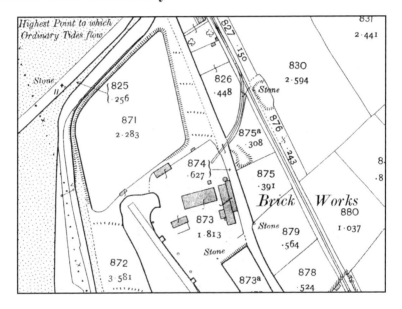

Devoran brickworks . © Crown Copyright 1907

Cornwall Brick, Tile and Trading Co. Ltd., Devoran
Grid Reference: SW719392
Marked on both the 1880 and 1907 maps of the Ordnance Survey maps, the works was situated to the west of the village and to the east of the Devoran and Chasewater Railway line and was served by a siding from the railway. An aerial photograph, possibly taken in 1930, shows the disused brickworks which are on the site of what is now a joinery works. Clay was obtained from quarry to the north of the works and brought to the site through a tunnel. The bricks are red in colour, with a frog.

Some whitish coloured bricks are known and these were probably made from mud taken from the nearby estuary. It is thought that brick making ceased here in 1900.

Brickmark: unknown

Mylor Brickworks, Mylor Bridge
Grid Reference: SW792365
Kelly's Directory for Mylor, 185(4?) records Edmonds, Stephen brick maker, Mylor bridge and Roberts, John brick maker, Ballere (sic.) Brickfields, Mylor Bridge.

Also extant is a lease of 1852 between Sir Charles Lemon and Stephen Edmonds, chemist and John Roberts, builder of Falmouth for 5 acres of land at Dowstall Moors (Grid Reference: SW801371). The lease also includes a kiln and dwelling adjoining a quay or wharf. It seems likely that the latter refers to Limekiln Quay, south east of Mylor Bridge, on the north side of Mylor Creek.

Mr. Roberts advert in The Penryn Advertiser on 3 February 1873, for the sale by auction of equipment and other materials of Mylor Brick Works in February 1873 gives us some idea of the scale of the brick making operation which had been carried out. The equipment offered for sale includes a pug mill, what might be crusher rolls and a brick making machine. Interestingly there is no mention of a brick kiln.

At Belleaire Farm there is some evidence of brick rubble in the garden and on land adjacent. It is thought that some of the bricks made here were used in the construction of Enys House.

Brickmark: maybe E & R FALMOUTH (E & R may refer to Edmonds & Roberts)

Mylor Brick and Tile Co., Angarrick, Mylor Bridge
Grid Reference: SW797375
Leases of 1852 [1], 1866 [2], 1886 [3] and 1900 [4] refer to sites at Cogos Tenement at Engarricke (presumably Angarrick) and part of Garrack Vean in the occupation of the Mylor Brick and Tile Company.

These records suggest that the company was operational from c.1850 until sometime after 1900.

Brickmark: unknown.

Swanpool/Pennance Works, Pennance in Budock
Grid Reference: SW803313 (approx.)
In 1805 it was recorded [5] that clay suitable for brick making had been found at Swanpool and that fine sand for use in conjunction with the clay, was available from a quarry nearby. It is thought that a brickworks exploiting these resources was started but was short lived. The site, which later was used for an arsenic works, is shown on a tithe map where Pennance Point Cottage now stands.

Brickmark: unknown

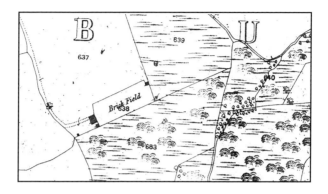

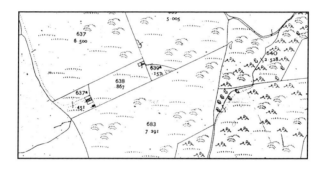

Top: *Part of the 1840 Tithe map marking what may have been the site of*
of Budock Brickworks.
Bottom: *Part of the O.S. Map, showing of the same area.*
© *Crown Copyright 1880*

Budock, near Tresooth
Grid Reference: SW772319
The 1840 Tithe map shows a field called "Brick Field", as well as marking what may be
a brick kiln which was occupied by J. Bone. The field is still marked on the 1887 edition
O.S. map. In 1887 W. Johns is recorded as a manufacturer of ordinary building bricks[6],
trading under the name Falmouth & Penryn Brickworks Co. and probably occupying the
same site. Nothing else is known.

The receiving book for West Wheal Lovell Mine records receiving bricks from the Penryn
Brick Works Co. in 1864 and 1865. This reference may refer to Budock.

5.2 Around Redruth

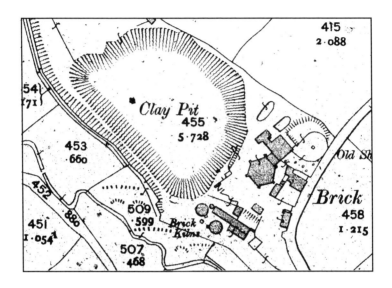

St. Day Brickworks © Crown Copyright 1907

St. Day Firebrick & China Clay Co. Ltd., St. Day
Grid Reference: SW728423
In advertisements dating from the last quarter of the 19th Century, the company is variously
referred to as: St. Day Firebrick and China Clay Manufacturing Co.; St. Day Firebrick
and Clay Co. Ltd. and St. Day Firebrick and China Clay Co. Ltd.

Small amounts of impure china clay may have been worked at St. Day to provide fireclay
for use in the construction of tin smelting furnaces long before Cookworthy opened his
workings on Tregonning Hill in 1746 [6]. Although in 1749 Josiah Wedgwood, looking
for potting clay rejected that at St. Day, he nevertheless took out a lease on the pit in
about 1775 with John Turner of Lane End. These partners and their successors worked
the pit, called Wheal Amelia, until the last decade of the 18th century, after which time
they were able to get sufficient clay from the St. Austell area.

The St. Day brickworks were started c.1860 by a Mr. Hawke, who was succeeded by
Captain Nettle of Truro who exported some of the clay produced during the decade
1876–1886, shipping it from Penryn. By 1874 a large kiln had been erected, probably
the hexagonal Hoffman kiln with a central chimney stack, which can be seen in many
published photographs. It can be seen on the map (hexagonal structure just south east of
clay pit), there were also two beehive kilns with their respective chimneys.

Other buildings which were used for brick making and drying can also be clearly seen on both maps and photographs. In 1910 the clay pit covered some 5.73 acres (2.32 hectares). Following the closure of the brickworks in 1912, there was spasmodic working for clay until its final closure in the late 1920's. The last manager of the works before it closed in 1912 was Fred Tamblyn. The fired clay products made at the St. Day works included: building bricks, stable paviours, tiles and firebricks of all sizes and patterns. They also supplied the mining industry with stack, cylinder and arch bricks. The cost of firebricks varied with time, thus in 1890 they were 18/9^d (93p) per 1000, between 1896 and 1899 they were 21/- (105p) to 23/- (£1.15p) per 1000, but by1905 they were only 10/6^d (52p). The bricks manufactured at St. Day were a buff or pale cream colour with a typical size of 8 ¾ " x 4 ¼" x 2 ½". Many were sold up-country and there was a thriving export market to France and other countries.

The Redruth and Chasewater Railway constructed a long loop at Caharrack, to serve as a siding for the works in 1874 and the closure of the brickworks in 1912 proved to be the death knell of the railway.

The site of the brickworks is now completely cleared, the clay pit is filled and now used as a sports facility [7].

Brickmark: S^T DAY and ST DAY
Lettering: 1 ½ inches and occasionally 2 inches high

A view of the St. Day Brickworks and clay pit, late 19th century.

St. Day Brick and Clay Co. representatives card and price list c.1880.
Top: *Front* Bottom: *Reverse.*

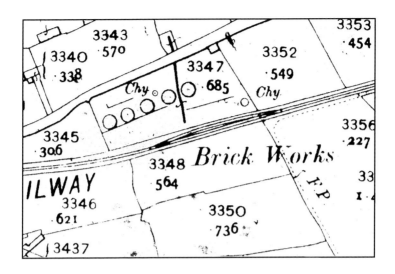

Pennance Brickworks © Crown Copyright 1907

The Pennance Fire-Clay & Brick Company [8], Pennance, Gwennap
Grid Reference: SW718404
The earliest documented lease is dated 24/3/1874 and the first working at the site was by Beer, Musgrave & Co. in 1875. In February of that year, adverts for the sale of firebricks and tiles were placed. A few bricks marked B.M. & Co. have been found here. The plan was to market china clay as well as bricks and to this end thickening pits and kiln tanks were installed. Bricks were made from the mica drag waste and burnt in two beehive kilns. By the mid-1880's clay production began to be phased out so that by 1885 the clay thickening pits and tanks were replaced by three more brick kilns. The firm was reorganised as the Carn Marth Brick & Clay Co. in 1885 and in 1888 it became known as the Vulcan Fire-Brick Co.

In September 1892 the Vulcan works and equipment was put up for sale at auction. In the mid-1890's the site was idle but worked again briefly in 1902 and again in 1906 and was closed permanently by 1910.

The clay, dug in a pit on Carn Marth, was derived from decomposed elvan and was taken through an adit, to the brickworks on the opposite side of the road. In 1880 there were three kilns served by two chimneys, whereas in 1910 there were five as seen on the accompanying map. Michell records that bricks from here were used in the Redruth Tin Smelting Co's. works [9].

Although the site has been cleared and is now used for housing, the entrance to the largely blocked adit could be seen just opposite the west side of Bolivar House. The clay pit itself was back filled by a local farmer in 1985.

Trevarth Fire Brick & Clay Company, NW of Trevarth, S of Ting Tang Mine
Grid Reference: SW728407
Shown on the 1878 Ordnance Survey map as disused, but not on the 1907 edition. This
brickworks started in 1873, was for sale in 1874 [10], advertised as follows:

> *"A valuable clay Sett to be sold by tender together with all necessary*
> *machinery and buildings suitable for the manufacture of bricks, tiles, etc.*
> *consisting of two newly-erected stone built kilns bound with iron. Crushing rollers,*
> *pug mill, hack-grounds, sheds, offices and other plant.*
>
> *The sett is situated in the Parish of Gwennap, and extends for upwards of*
> *half a mile in length over a large bed of elvan clay, of exceptionally high quality*
> *for the purpose of brick, tile and coarse pottery manufacture.*
>
> *The Redruth and Devoran Mineral Railway run along the boundary of the*
> *Sett, by which supplies can be obtained. The location is central to a large mining*
> *district, which constitutes a ready market for the products. There is a constant*
> *supply of water at all seasons.*
>
> *The purchaser will have the option of taking, at a valuation, the present*
> *working stock of brick. Apply to F. Savage of Gwennap for samples of clay and*
> *brick, analysis of clay, conditions of sale, etc."*

It is doubtful if the works ever reopened and only the small flooded clay pit remains.

Brickmark: TREVARTH (very rare)

Ting Tang
Grid Reference SW730407
An elvan dyke which appears near Trevarth and is met with in the workings of Ting
Tang mine has been reported. The elvan is decomposed at the surface and some clay was
used in about 1840 for the manufacture of fire bricks [11]. No more is known but there
is a shallow, drained pit of clay material on the east side of the Carharrack association
football ground which might have been used. This is close to Trevarth but the pits are
separate. There are no relics of buildings or kilns for Ting Tang which according to the
reference predates Trevarth.

United Downs
Grid Reference SW746421 (estimated)
A map [12] of the United Downs area made in 1821 shows a square open ended building
labelled 'brick kiln'. The tithe map of the area in 1839 shows no structure resembling
the kiln of 1821. We can only speculate that bricks were made using local decomposed
elvan. A possible clay source not far away is an elvan worked at Sparry Bottom in a linear
cutting (Grid Reference SW395138).

Redruth, adjoining Pedn-an-Drea Mine (marked on the 1887 edition O.S. Map)
Grid Reference: SW704424 (approx.)
Works for making crucibles were established in about 1760 by John Juleff at Trewirgie, situated between Trewirgie Road and Church Lane [13]. This works closed prior to 1866 when operations were moved to Redruth. John was succeeded by his sons John and David Juleff. In Kelley's Directory for 1873 there is an advertisement for 'John Juleff Cornish Plumbago Crucible maker and Richard Juleff brick maker' The brick range included 'muffers, scorifiers, special bricks and covers for assay furnaces etc.' This echoes the production of bricks at the Calenick crucible works. According to Percy [14] large crucibles were made from Teignmouth clay (S. Devon ball clay) 1 part, Poole clay (Dorset ball clay) 1 part and sand from St. Agnes Beacon (silica) 2 parts. No further information found.

Lizard Brick & Tile Works [15], Cross Common
Grid Reference: SW707125
This works, at Cross Common, near the Lizard in Landewedneck, was managed by Silvanus W. Jenkin and Pearse Jenkin, on behalf of T. J. Agar Robartes and was operational between 1851 and 1867. Both brick and drainage tiles were manufactured. The raw material was probably a loess obtained nearby and from the Lizard Downs, while coal was delivered by sea, at Church Cove. There is a record of firebricks purchased from Stourbridge, to rebuild the kiln in February 1864.

The bright red bricks produced here were used locally and some examples of their use can still be found. It has been recorded that several thousand bricks were supplied for the building of Druids Hall, Redruth in 1859. Parts of the building still survive and some red brick dressings may be all that remains of the Lizard bricks.

Grade Church nearby (Grid Reference SW713144), almost completely rebuilt in 1862, has brick dressings on the windows of the south side of the nave and a sedilia with red brick arches and dressings. It seems likely that Lizard brick was used.

Brickmark: unknown

Unmarked wedge shaped brick made at the Lizard works. Note that the header face of this brick has been over burnt and is vitrified (Left)..

Top: *Lizard Brick & Tile Works manager's house and works office at Cross Common, Lizard. Built c 1855 of brick made at the works.*
 Bottom: *Detail of the coping on the wall surrounding the garden of the house.*

E & R FALMOUTH (EDMONDS & ROBERTS)   PENNANCE, REDRUTH

ST. DAY (FIREBRICK)

ST. DAY (BOILER SEATING)

NEWTOWN BRICKWORKS

NEWTOWN BRICKWORKS

WHEAL GREY (WILLIAM ARGAL)

TREGONING HILL
(WILLIAM ARGAL)

Some Brickmarks of West Cornwall works.

5.3 Around Penzance

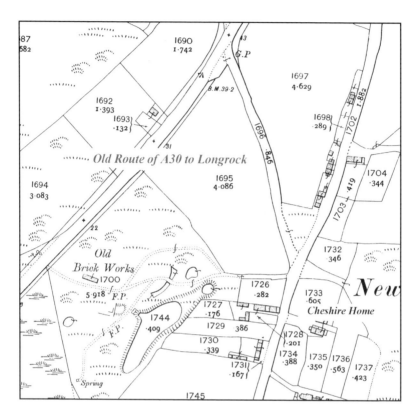

Site of the Acme Brick & Tile Co. works at Newtown, Marazion.
In order to simplify interpretation, the line of the old A30(T) is labelled as
is the approximate site of the Cheshire Home. © *Crown Copyright 1907*

BRICK   YARD   AND   WORKS,
(Coloured Brown on Plan)

Occupying about

8 a.   :   2 r.   :   30 p.

In the occupation of THE ACME BRICK AND TILE Co., LIMITED. The tenancy agreement reserves a
Surface rent of £3 3s. for every acre used, and a minimum Royalty of £2 10s. a quarter, and provides
that about 11a. 2r. 6p. to the north-west of and about 15a. 2r. 36p. to the south of the land coloured
brown on the plan, may be used for making bricks. The Farm Tenant is entitled to a reduction
of rent at the rate of £1 per acre for any land so taken.

Part of a sale document relating to property in the Parish of Ludgvan, Cornwall. This
gives details of the sale of the Acme Brickworks. Sadly there is no date, although it must
have been after 1893.

Acme Brick & Tile Co., Newtown, Marazion
Grid Reference: SW508316
Recorded as being operated by Richard Williams in 1883 and advertised in Kelly's
Directory as Newtown Brickworks, Ludgvan, with a similar entry in the 1889 Directory.
Bricks from this early working are marked "Newtown Ludgvan". Later, in 1893, the
Kelly's entry tells us that the site was operated by the Acme Brick & Tile Co. with Richard
Mathews as proprietor. In 1897 Edward Mitchel is recorded as manager. The brickmark
changed to "Acme" when Mathews took over.

The site of the works is in a field opposite the Cheshire Home in Newtown, with clay being
obtained nearby [16]. As we shall see later clay may also have been brought from the Castle
working on Tonkin Downs. In the "Industries of Penzance and its Neighbourhood", it is recorded
that there were two kilns [17], although the map suggests that there was one rectangular kiln.

Dark coloured bricks whose typical size is 9 ½ inches x 2 ½ inches x 4 ¼ inches bearing
the "ACME" mark are fairly common in West Cornwall. The "NEWTOWN/LUDGVAN"
mark is rarely seen.

Brickmarks: NEWTOWN/LUDGVAN & ACME

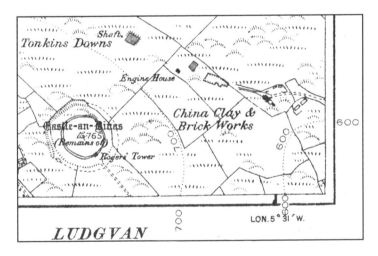

Site of Castle Brickworks © Crown Copyright 1888

Castle, Tonkin Downs between Castle-an-Dinas Quarry and Higher Trenowin, near
Nancledra.
Grid Reference: SW488351
Little is known of these brickworks which are marked on the 1888 edition O.S. map as a
"China Clay and Brick Works" and simply as an "Old Clay Pit" on the 1906 revised
edition. The only surviving evidence of a works here today is a large depression at the site
of the clay pit and some boggy areas beyond, where water for washing the clay might

have been ponded. This working was operational between 1870 and 1900.

Although Smith [18] records that the brickmark 'CASTLE' was used, no examples have been found. This record is contrary to the findings of a recent visit to the site where no direct evidence of a kiln was found. It may be that the clay was taken to the brickworks of the Acme Brick and Tile Co. at Newtown, Marazion, nearby.

Wheal Grey China Clay & Tin Co., Tresowes Green, east of Germoe
Grid Reference: SW591291

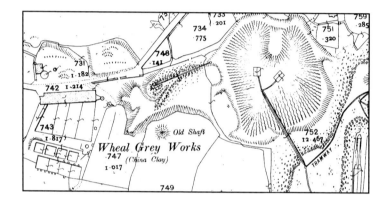

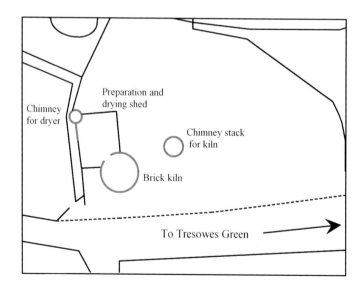

Wheal Grey Clay and Brickworks (in top left hand corner).
Top: *O.S. map © Crown Copyright 1907*
Bottom: *Sketch map based on visit to the site in April 2002.*

Operational between 1878 and c.1900, the brickworks are to the west of the china clay pit at Wheal Grey and on the opposite side of the minor road into the village. This enterprise was owned and managed by William Argall of Breage, Helston; who built a Scrivener Kiln here in 1878. Argall continued to operate here until his retirement in 1893 when the leases were acquired by Messrs. Holman, Harvey and Thomas, who were in turn were bought out by Lovering & Co.

The kiln and its associated chimney as well as the drying shed with part of its chimney, still survive and are marked in grey on the map. The buildings are situated immediately north of the original china clay tanks and clay dry. The brick kiln and its associated chimney stack are still extant although rather overgrown. It should be noted that Crofts [19] recorded two kilns in the account quoted earlier (Chapter 2), whereas the evidence on the ground and from the published O.S. maps suggests that there was only a single kiln. The drying area and its associated chimney are covered in ivy and the undergrowth effectively prevents a close examination of either structure.

The bricks are generally dark red in colour and are 9 ¼ inches x 4 ¼ inches x 2 ¾ inches in size.

Brick mark: W.A (note that there is normally a stop between W and A)

Wheal Grey, view of the chimney and outer wall of part of the drying area.

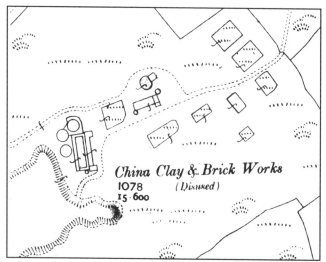

Tregonning Hill Clay and Brickworks

© Crown Copyright 1907

Tregonning Hill Clay and Brickworks, Tregonning Hill between Godolphin Cross and Breage.

Grid Reference: SW605299

The works, operational from 1871 until c1900, was supplied with clay from the historically important china clay pits on Tregonning Hill, whose leases were held at this time by W. Harvey, William Argall and John Toy. There are two contemporary published accounts of this works, written in 1878 and 1883 [20]. In the 1883 account a rectangular or Scotch Kiln is recorded, while today the only surviving structure on the site is a circular beehive or Scrivener Kiln (illustrated p. 116). The map clearly shows several miscellaneous rectangular buildings any one of which could have been the Scotch Kiln. The most likely candidate is the rectangular structure roughly in the centre of the map, which appears to have chimneys associated with it at the south west and north east ends. Another possible interpretation is that this building was used for brick manufacture and partial drying as already described for the small works at Carkeet (Chapter 4).

Whatever this building was used for, it is certain that the circular building with a chimney immediately to the north, is the surviving beehive kiln. The rectangular and circular buildings nearest the clay pit are most likely to have been associated with the extraction and thickening of the china clay: i.e. they are circular settling tanks with an associated rectangular clay dry.

Elsewhere on the site there are eight miscellaneous rectangular buildings, which may or may not have been associated with brick and clay industry on the site.

Bricks from this works were buff in colour.

Brickmarks: TREGONNING HILL and possibly W.A

END NOTES

1   Cornwall Record Office. Reference: WH530/1 and WH530/2
2   Cornwall Record Office. Reference: WH531
3   Cornwall Record Office. Reference: WH532
4   Cornwall Record Office. Reference: WH540
5   Royal Cornwall Gazette 23 March 1805
6   R. N. Worth 1887 Clays and Fictile Manufacturers of Cornwall and Devon.
     Royal Cornwall Polytechnic Society
7   John Pendrill-Church 1982 China Clay In West Cornwall.
     A report for ECC International, St. Austell. Reference: LHB 030182
8   Schwartz S. & Parker R. 1998 Lanner a Cornish Mining Parish. Halsgrove,
     Tiverton. Chapter 6, p.115ff.
9   Michell F. 1978 Annals of an Ancient Cornish Town - Redruth. Dyllansow Truran,
     Redruth 247pp. p.236
10   Royal Cornwall Gazette. 25 July 1884
11   C. C. James 1949 History of Gwennap Published by the author, Penzance p.156
     and Schwartz S. & Parker R. 1998 Lanner a Cornish Mining Parish. Halsgrove,
     Tiverton. Chapter 6, p.116
12   CRO Map LEE24 (1821)
13   Ibid. p.165
14   Percy 1875 Metallurgy, p.118
15   R. M. Phillips, Journal of the Lizard Field Club 1963, pp 16-17 and 1965,
     pp.14-15
16   Information from members of the Marazion Old Cornwall Society
17   The Cornishman. 10 May 1883
18   J. R. Smith, 1987. p.21
19   The Cornishman. 10 May 1883
20   Royal Cornwall Gazette, 15 February 1878 and The Cornishman of 10 May 1883

Tregonning Hill Brickworks. The extant beehive 'Scrivener' kiln. Top: *General view.* Bottom: *Detail inside of the kiln, showing vitrification of the lining.*

CHAPTER 6

ESTATE AND MINOR BRICKWORKS

In this chapter we will consider some of the smaller and often more poorly recorded brickworks in Cornwall. For many of these the precise location of the kiln or burning site or even the source of the raw materials is unknown. This is in no way a complete list and research in places like the Cornwall Record Office (CRO) and the literature will no doubt uncover more examples.

We also record here the many early brick making campaigns associated with the building or rebuilding of houses or walled gardens by the gentry of Cornwall. The majority of these estate brickworks are early in date and the methods of firing the clay in some cases is not documented so we have to assume that clamp firing was carried out. Some of these building works are extant although others have long since been pulled down. Again we expect that future research will probably discover more detail.

Antony House (National Trust), near Torpoint.
Grid Reference SX418563
The building of the house commenced in 1711 under the direction of Sir William Carew (1689 - 1744), and was completed c 1721. In October 1713 an Exeter master-builder was given the contract to construct walls for a new garden at Antony [1]. Some 400,000 bricks were required and these were to be fired on the site. The dovecote near the house is also built of red brick, and is thought to be coeval.

Trewardale, near Blisland.
Grid Reference SX103717
In a report to the Royal Cornwall Polytechnic Society in 1868 the Rev. C. M. Edward Collins of Trewardale, a country house near Blisland, reported that, 'I have a garden wall and, until lately, had a carriage house built with brick, which I have ascertained were made on the place, exactly a century since'. Edward Collins was a keen observer of clay working in the Temple area and an advocate of potteries in Cornwall on the lines of the Torquay Potteries. There is nothing now to be seen of his bricks, the carriage house is rebuilt in granite and the wall has gone. If the bricks referred to were made in the 18th century they may have been of poor quality due to lack of experience although they would come into the period referred to by Borlase in his Natural History [2].

Stowe House near Kilkhampton
Grid Reference SS21201130
At Stowe in north Cornwall a large house was built by 1679 for Sir John Grenville, the third son of Sir Bevil Grenville. This house replaced a medieval manor house and appears to have been an early example of brick building in Cornwall. According to Lysons it was described by Dr. William Borlase, in a work since lost, as 'by far the noblest house in the west of England'. In a diary of John Loveday it is described as, 'the finest seat in these Western Parts' and 'Tis a brick house'. Further evidence of it being brick built comes from a brick making contract of 1676 which contains a reference to make and burn bricks 'as John Rumbold did make for John Fitch at Stowe in ye County of Cornwall'...........'in ye same moulds for bigness'.

Sir John Grenville became Earl of Bath and died in 1701 at Stowe. It seems that his family considered the house with its bleak cliff side location and distance from London, a liability and the house became neglected. In 1739 the house was demolished and the building materials recovered were sold. Charles Henderson records seeing a 'Paper showing a plan of bricks at Stowe arranged in heaps c.1750' [3].

At Stowe Barton, erected on the site of the stables, are the high walls of the carriage wash, but these are built of stone. These are the only extant remains of Stowe House.

Kilkhampton
Grid Reference SS25531115
In Cornish Archaeology [4] a parochial check list of antiquities for Kilkhampton refers to a brick field with no remains extant a few miles east of Stowe.

Lostwithiel, Restormel Farm (Duchy of Cornwall property).
Grid Reference SX102616 (approx.)
Red bricks have been discovered in the first field on the west side of the road as the farm is passed. The field adjacent was called Brick Field, which implies that it was formerly used to burn bricks. The buildings on the farm which are made from this brick include a mill, a Dutch Barn (part) and a walled garden (illustrated, p.120). The present tenant (Mr. Steven Hutchins) has told us that the buildings were constructed during the period of a lease taken out by the Robartes family c.1820 The Dutch Barn was erected by Ann Agar to commemorate the 21st birthday of her son, Thomas James Agar (1808 - 82). These buildings are probably all coeval which puts the date of the brick making and building operation here at around 1829. The bricks here are slightly thinner than normal.

Tregullon, near Bodmin
Grid Reference SX064450
Red clay was discovered near at Tregullon near Bodmin in 1893. A report tells that Mr. Henry Dennis of the Hafod brick and terracotta works at Ruabon in North Wales

had tested the Tregullon Clay and it was adjudged to be a potter's clay which was also suitable for terracotta.

The site at Tregullon is in an area where copper, tin and iron ores were raised and the red clay may have had value as an iron ore. Also reported in 1893 [5] were trials made to eight feet in solid clay but the extent of the bed was not assessed. It was further stated that Lord Robartes, of Lanhydrock, had granted a lease on favourable terms but no evidence of brick or terracotta manufacture has been found.

Heligan House, St. Ewe
Grid Reference SX000465
Built between 1695 and 1720, Heligan was brick-built, using bricks made on site. It is recorded that the 300,000 bricks needed to build the house, were made from clay dug on the estate and burnt in-situ by Richard Burges, at a cost of 5/- (25p) per 1000 [6]. The house walls are now rendered and the brickwork can no longer be seen. Nearby in the gardens (Lost Gardens of Heligan), the recently uncovered and cleaned walls of the Italian Garden, Kitchen and Flower Garden and their associated outbuildings are built from a red/brown colour brick. The possible dates for these structures are: Flower Garden c.1710, Citrus House c.1800, Melon Garden c.1820 and Beeboles c.1850. Thus it seems likely that the bricks of the Flower Garden walls are the same as those used to build the house.

Boscundle, just north of the A390, 1 mile east of St. Austell
Grid Reference SX049531 (exact location not known)
There are a number of leases held in the Cornwall County Record Office which refer to brick and tile making in this low lying area and recording a kiln or kilns used for this purpose. The earliest lease is dated 1769.

Redmoor, Between Lanlivery and Lostwithiel
Grid Reference: Exact location unknown
An agreement [7] dated October 1808 between William Jenkins and Neville Norway of Lostwithiel (limekiln owner), granted permission for Norway to make bricks on Redmoor, with a 'land leave' (charge) of 1/- (5p) per 1000 bricks. This may be the Maudlin Stone, Ochre & Brickworks listed in Kelly's 1897 Directory, managed by George R. Bellamy of Bodmin.

Portmellon
Grid Reference SX015438 (approx.)
Brickworks near the stream in Portmellon are reputed to have produced "highly coloured bricks" and examples can be seen as dressings to old houses in the village. The raw material came from Carvinick, near Gorran Haven (Grid reference SX000416), where in 1872 a sett was started to "dig, work and search for yellow ochre and brick-clay in Carvinick (sic) Meadow [8]. Other brick making material was also obtained from a sett on nearby 'Great Moor'.

Restormel Farm, Lostwithiel.

Two views of the Mill building, now used for general farm purposes and constructed from brick burnt on the farm, c.1829. Flemish bond throughout.
Photographed by kind permission of Mr. Steven Hutchins, tenant farmer.
Left: *Front view.*
Below: *Side and rear view.*

Sticker, on edge of bypass road
Grid Reference SW982508
While carrying out a survey along the ground cleared for the Sticker bypass, the Cornwall Archaeological Unit discovered a brick-firing site, with a clay floor on which bricks would have been fired in a clamp. Magnetic dating suggests that this working may date from c.1810 and is associated with house building in Sticker. Nearby is a marshy area, from which grey clay appears to have been dug and which is partly back filled with old hand made bricks. The bricks are of an orange colour with impurities including small pieces of coal and have no frog.

Penans or Pennance Farm, between Hewaswater and Grampound
Grid Reference SW955489
An old farmhouse and brick walled garden at Penans between Hewaswater and Grampound has been noted by Hitchens (1824) and others.

The use of some bricks in the older farmhouse here is interesting but of more significance are the two extensive brick walled areas, now somewhat ruinous, by the farm. The farm houses and adjacent walled areas are now 'listed'. A summary of the history of the farm is given by Bane and Oliver, 1998 [9] and there is a reference to its part in the history of the Quaker movement in Hodgkin 1927. A report for English Heritage says that the garden walls may have been in existence as early as 1677. This would make it one of the earliest, locally made brick structure in Cornwall of which we are aware.

The bricks found are unmarked, red to white in colour and uneven along their edges. They suggest the use of clay head or loess from a nearby marshy area to the west of the farm where there were probably ponds. The present main 'turnpike' road cut through the avenue later on in the 18th century. Hitchens (1824), tells that to maintain the avenue a lofty arch formed of brick was constructed to bridge the road but this arch was taken down in the 1780's 'to prevent accidents' and most of the trees have since gone except perhaps for some lime trees close to the former pond area which lay to the western end of the avenue.

Brick making here might have been undertaken by farm workers using clamp firing. However accounts tell that much of the development of the walled garden was undertaken by Henry Huddy who 'foolishly lavished' this estate. He might have imported brick makers with no regard to their cost. The brick bridge would certainly have been novel in it's day but does not seem to have inspired any recording by artists or draughtsmen.

Trewithen House, Probus
Grid Reference SW914475
The front of Trewithen House, designed by Thomas Edwards for Philip Hawkins c.1715, was built of brick, which was subsequently rendered in 1948. These bricks were made

from blue clay dug on the estate and burnt on site **[10]**. There are also 2 detached wings built of pink-red brick, which were added later, probably in about 1740. Again these bricks were made and burnt on the site.

Gerrans, Methers Collyn
Grid Reference SW874367
A brickworks owned by James Thomas was started here c.1888 and managed by a Mr. Alderman and his sons, who may have come to the parish to set up the works which originally produced bricks to build a wing on the south side of the Thomas's farm house at Methers Collyn. Other buildings of note built from these bricks are Pollaughan farm house and farm buildings at Methers Collyn, Tregassa and Treluggan. The clay pit and kiln (probably a beehive kiln) are reputed to be in a field nearby although there is no evidence to be seen today. Local residents confirm that the bricks made here were of high quality and red coloured **[11]**.

Brickmark: J T G (James Thomas, Gerrans)

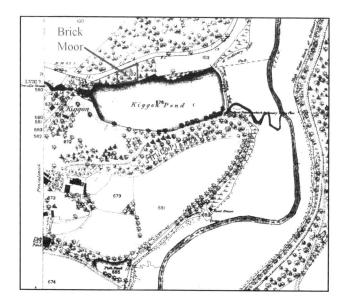

The site of a possible brickworks at Polsue. See Brick Moor, top left.

Polsue, St. Erme
Grid Reference SW859456
Land between the Truro - Tresillian road and Kiggon Creek or Pond, was commonly called "Brick Moor' **[12]**. There is no record of any kilns in the area and this could have been the site of a local works, with the bricks being burnt in a clamp.

It is possible that the bricks made here were used to build Trehane House.

Woodcock Corner - Between Truro and Tresillian
Grid Reference SW846462
The site of a brick clamp was discovered when soil was stripped away during road widening in the 1990's. Some remains of coarse, badly mixed bricks were found. They contained white clay fragments and white quartz chips, showing that they were badly mixed, probably by the primitive method of puddling with bare feet. Part of the nearby Pencalenick House is known to be brick built, using bricks which show similar characteristics to those found at Woodcock Corner. These were probably transported from where they were made to the house, along a track which has now almost disappeared.

Truro, St. Clement - Park Farm
Grid Reference SW842437
The old house known as Park was rebuilt in the 18th century as a farmhouse, using some bricks made on the farm. As field number 1487, to the south west of the farm (Tithe Map, 1844) is called brick meadow [13], it is assumed that the clay for these bricks was dug there.

Trefusis House, near Flushing
Grid Reference: SW816336
It is suggested [14] that a subway leading south from the house toward the sea is lined with bricks made from clay dug on the estate.
This construction is related to the Georgian house built in the early 18th century, which fell into disrepair and was subsequently rebuilt in 1890.

Part of the walled garden at Trelowarren House, built in the mid-17th century.

Examples of estate made bricks.
Top: *Heligan, walled garden.*
Middle: *Barn at Restormel Farm.*
Bottom: *Trelowarren, walled garden.*

Trelowarren House, Gweek

Grid Reference: SW722238

Remains of a possible brick making site have been found on Gilly Farm. The site is close to the north side, of the Helston – St. Keverne road (B3293) and Gilly Farm, near to Garras, about 1 mile. south west of Trelowarren House at SW713233. To the south of the road, situated in Chygarkye Wood, there are old marl pits, which were possibly the source of the raw material. The present day evidence of brick making is in a field once known as Brickfield [15], a marshy area where broken bricks of a bright orange colour and pieces of slag have been found. There also appears to be the remains of a stockpile of marl used by the brick makers on the edge of the field. In 1977 Mrs. Margaret Hunt recorded the existence of a large oval surround standing 8 – 12" (20 - 30 cms.) high, with much clinker and bricks scattered around nearby [16].

The brickworks is thought to have been in use between 1630 and 1660 when the brick-walled garden was constructed and the north side of Trelowarren House[17] was rebuilt using brick (illustrated p.124).

Tehidy House, approx. 1 mile north of Camborne

Grid Reference: SW648434

In 1734, John Pendarves Basset commenced the rebuilding of the Tehidy Mansion, probably replacing an earlier, Tudor manor house. Surviving accounts show that preparations began in April 1734, when a brick maker was paid to survey the area for clay which would be suitable for brick making. This clay may have been found at nearby Higher Melrose, Illogan, as there is an area here which was referred to as Brick Moor in records from 1805. By July 1734 brick making by "James the Bricker" assisted by estate staff was in full swing. It is recorded that the bricks were transported to a Brick House (in Cornwall a Brick House probably refers to a Scotch kiln), by barrow.

The location of this kiln is not recorded. Initially the bricks were fired using furze, wood and cow dung, as fuel. Probably because of this, the kiln could not produce bricks at the rate required for the building campaign and in July 1735, 12,000 bricks were shipped from London and landed at Hayle. By 1738 the brick kiln was being fired using imported coal [18].

Published photographs of Tehidy House show that it was a stone faced building, so that it seems likely that the bricks were used internally. The walled kitchen gardens, as in other Cornish houses of this period, were built of brick manufactured on the estate.

END NOTES

1   National Trust
2   Borlase Nat. Hist., 1758, p.63
3   The notes on Stowe House are based on articles by G. M. Trinick in the Royal Inst. Cornwall Journals for 1979 and 1986/87, which are fully referenced
4   Cornish Archaeology No. 14, 1975
5   British Clayworker, July 1893, p.75
6   Heligan Accounts 1692. Cornwall Record Office. Reference: T128415
7   Hamilton Jenkin Letter Book HJ/1/9 held by the Royal Inst. Cornwall
7   Cornwall Record Office. Reference: CF3873
9   Bane & Oliver 1998 The book of Grampound with Creed. Halsgrove
10 McCabe H. "Houses and Gardens of Cornwall" 162 pp., 1988, Tabb House, Padstow. p.89ff
11 Hilary Thompson, Methers Collyn Brickworks. Roseland Magazine, March 1992
12 C. R. O. TLP146, 1839 & TLP260, 1839
13 In and Around St. Clement Churchtown. Truro Buildings Research Group. 1999, pp.61-63
14 Redwood, 1987 Trefusis Territory. P.11
15 Letter from John Vyvyan to Mrs. Margaret Hunt, dated 13 November 1991
16 Letter from Mrs. Margaret Hunt to Charles Thurlow 19 September 1993
17 Letter from John Vyvyan to Mrs. Margaret Hunt, dated 13 November 1991
18 This information mainly from: Tangye, M. "Tehidy and the Bassets – the rise and fall of a great Cornish family", 88pp. 2002 edition, Truran, Truro

CHAPTER 7

OTHER BURNT CLAY PRODUCTS

Although bricks of various types such as building, engineering, fire, glazed and stack [1] bricks formed the main output of Cornish brickworks, many other burnt clay products were made. For example the introduction from the 1830's of coal fired pan kilns which were used to dry china clay, brought about a demand for porous tiles to pave the heated bed of the kiln. As the use of pan kilns spread, the demand for these tiles increased and this, coupled with the need to renew them at frequent intervals, gave rise to a steady market for the product. Indeed, the last brickworks to close in Cornwall, had survived simply through supplying tiles to the last of the pan kilns used. Modern drying methods do not involve the use of these kilns and the manufacture of tiles ceased.

Another important product of the Cornish brick industry was decorated architectural terracotta, which was largely, although not exclusively, manufactured at works in the Tamar Valley. Glazed terracotta known as faience was not manufactured in Cornwall except perhaps at Carkeet. Other building materials such as those used for roofing were also made, although the majority of the Counties requirements were imported from up-country and in particular from Bridgwater in Somerset. In the remainder of this chapter we will look in more detail at the whole range of burnt clay products, other than bricks, made at Cornish brickworks.

7.1 Architectural Terracotta

The first burnt clay product other than brick is architectural terracotta [2]. Terracotta was originally used in the 18th century for both classical and contemporary ornaments and by 1839 the name was being applied to both architectural and sculptural works made from fired clay. Its use as an architectural material reached its peak in the penultimate decade of the 19th century, when it was deemed to be of a higher class than ordinary brick, yet cheaper than stone. The widespread use of the material was promoted as a solution to the detrimental effects of smog and fire [3].

Terracotta is still manufactured in the United Kingdom and is made by pressing clay into a prepared mould made from a plaster model. The moulded clay is then allowed to become leather hard (as in brick manufacture), before being fired. The finished material is designed to be integral with standard brickwork and

The Art School, Morab Road, Penzance.

Honey Street, Bodmin.

Venning's Fountain, Callington

Laninval House, Bodmin

Above: St. Nicholas Street, Bodmin
Left: Freemasons Hall, Bodmin

Examples of terracotta which show the variety of colours which can be found.
Only the examples from Venning's Fountain were made in Cornwall.

Examples of the use of architectural terracotta on some Cornish buildings.
Top Left: *Honey Street, Bodmin.* Top Centre: *Fore Street Marazion.*
Top Right: *Faience, Commercial Street, Camborne.*
Bottom: *The Art School, Morab Road, Penzance. None made in Cornwall.*

therefore comes in a number of standard sizes. It can take several forms such as plain or decorated slabs, shields or medallions. Sizes recorded from examples of Cornish terracotta found on buildings in County include: 17 x 6 inches (43.2 x 15.2 cms.) and 6 inches, 9 ½ inches and 12 inches square (15.2 cms., 24.1 cms. and 30.5 cms.). The colour of terracotta can vary depending on the clay from which it is manufactured or whether a glaze has been applied. Cornish brickworks which are recorded as having manufactured or had ambitions to make terracotta include Phoenix, Tamar, Millbrook, Carkeet, Grampound Road and Tregonning Hill. Much of the output from works in east Cornwall was exported. For example Phoenix terracotta went to Brighton.

Terracotta can be found on a number of buildings throughout the County, although there are very few where the manufacturer can be pinpointed with any degree of certainty, particularly in the case of up-country manufacturers. Exceptions are the Cornwall Farmers Ltd. building, now the Old Ale House, Quay Street, Truro (opposite); the Headland Hotel, Newquay, Laninval House near Bodmin and the St. Austell Bank (NatWest), all designed by the Cornish architect Silvanus Trevail and built toward the end of the 19th century. The buildings mentioned are all examples of the use of dark red terracotta which was Trevail's favourite decorative materials and was probably made by Henry Dennis [4], Ruabon, North Wales. In Bodmin for example, the Freemasons Hall, St. Nicholas Street, is decorated with Doulton cream terracotta.

Many other buildings which incorporate architectural terracotta can be found throughout Cornwall, where the manufacturer cannot be identified. Examples include commercial properties which can be seen in Bodmin, Honey Street; Camborne, Trelowarren Street and Commercial Street; Marazion, Fore Street; Penzance, Green Market and Morrab Road; Redruth, West End and Fore Street. Other types of property include: Lostwithiel Social Club, Fore Street; St. Ives, Godrevey Guest House, Trelyon Avenue. The Star Inn on the A30 at Crowlas is constructed in red brick with plain red terracotta used as dressings for quoins, windows and doors. Some examples are illustrated on p. 129.

Callington is one of the few towns in Cornwall where locally produced terracotta has been used, and where we can be fairly certain of its source. There are several examples. The best example is Venning's Fountain, situated just outside the town on Launceston Road. The base of the fountain is constructed from glazed white brick, with a capping of bull nosed blue bricks, both of which were probably made at the Tamar Works. The stepped, square fountain shows three sizes of decorative tile and displays many different patterns and these are illustrated on p.132. The tiles are recorded as being made at the Phoenix works [5]. Although the photographs are not to scale the size at which they are reproduced illustrates the 3 sizes: 12 inches (30 cms.), 9 ½ inches (24 cms.) and 6 inches (15 cms.) square. The largest sized, lower tier is all of one pattern , which is similar to the two intermediate tiers. The penultimate tier has a slightly different pattern, while the top tier is quite different and has several different patterns four of which are illustrated. Physically the top row of tiles appear to differ from those below

Cornwall Farmers Ltd. building, Quay Street, Truro. Built c1900 in cream and grey brick, it has dramatic red terracotta dressings. Designed by the Cornish architect Silvanus Trevail, the terracotta was probably made by Henry Dennis, Ruabon.

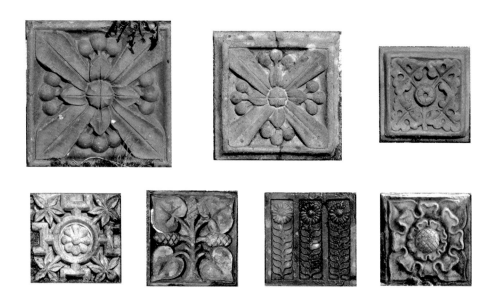

Examples of terracotta tiles used on Venning's Fountain, Callington.
These architectural terracotta tiles were made at the Phoenix works, while the brick
built base uses Tamar white glazed and bull nosed, blue engineering brick.
Bottom: *General view of the fountain.* Top: *Examples of the patterns of individual*
tiles, reproduced in proportion. Top left: *from the lowest tier.* Middle left: *from the*
two centre tiers. Remainder from the top two tiers.

*Examples of architectural terracotta. made by the Phoenix Vitrified Paving &
Firebrick Co. Used as detailing on domestic accommodation above a shop on
the corner of Liskeard Road, Callington. The property was built 1855.*
Top: *Front elevation.* Below: *Detail of some patterns used.*

Examples of architectural terracotta made by the Tamar Firebrick & Clay Co.
used as detailing on a Victorian toll house, Saltash Road, Callington.
Top: *Front elevation.*
Below: *Details of some patterns used to decorate the building.*

and may be made by a different manufacturer, in any event they do not appear to be original. Another building, originally an ironmongers (now a Spar Supermarket) built in 1855 on the site of the old Guildhall and is situated at the corner of Liskeard Road, almost opposite the church (illustrated on p.133). This building constructed c.1855, is of red brick with bands of decorative red terracotta made at the Phoenix works. Finally, on the Saltash Road is a Victorian toll house, which is also recorded as being decorated with Phoenix tiles [6]. However on a recent visit, loose tiles were seen in the garden showing the mark of the Tamar factory. This conclusion is further borne out by comparing the patterns illustrated with Frank Booker's photograph of discarded terracotta tiles found on the site of Tamar Firebrick and Tile Works [7] in the 1960's.

An example of terracotta which, because of marks on the reverse face, can be attributed to the Tamar Firebrick & Clay Co. can be seen in Liskeard. They form a garden edging on the front of a house at the Greenbank Road - Pound Street junction. These decorated border tiles are red in colour with a grape and vine leaf pattern The face measure 17 x 6 inches (43.2 x 15.2 cms.) and they are approximately 4 inches (10 cms.) thick.

Elsewhere in Liskeard, a house at Hong Kong, Old Road, built by Mr. John Harris c.1900, has a pink coloured (now cream painted) decorative shield on the wall of an outhouse facing the road. This is recorded as having been made at the Carkeet brickworks [8].

Terracotta ornament.
Left: *Plaque, mid 19th century, on the old Drill Hall (now the Town Hall), St. Just. Manufacturer unknown.*
Right: *Shield, C.1900 on house. Hong Kong, Old Road, Liskeard. Manufactured at the Carkeet brickworks (see above).*

Before leaving this section on architectural terracotta we must mention another product known as Coade Stone, so named after its manufacturer Eleanor Coade who came from Lyme Regis and manufactured 'artificial stone' in Lambeth, London. Coade Stone was a fired fictile product used to produce architectural decoration. It is much stronger and more weather resistant than traditional terracotta, due to the nature of the raw constituents and the manufacturing process. The earliest Coade Stone was produced in the 1770's and production continued until the 1830's, some years after Eleanor's death.

The recipe for Coade Stone was thought to have been lost when Eleanor died. However research in the 1980's [9] has shown that it is a mixture of clay (50%), crushed stoneware, flint, fine sand and crushed soda glass. These were mixed and finely ground to give a plastic mixture which was then pressed into moulds, prior to firing at 1100° centigrade for four days. The resulting objects were hardly distinguishable from natural stone and in some cases stood up to the weather and atmospheric pollution better. It had been assumed from the light colour of the finished product that the clay used was Cornish china clay but later research showed that it was a ball clay from Devon or Dorset.

In a comprehensive book on the subject Alison Kelly indicates how extensively the product was used throughout the country and abroad, by many of the foremost architects. In a gazetteer listing the recorded uses of Coade Stone she has identified eleven instances in Cornwall were Coade Stone has been used [10]. This list is not definitive and others may be found during future research. Examples of decorative Coade Stone from Truro are illustrated below.

Examples of Coade Stone decoration on the Assembly Rooms and Theatre, Truro. Built 1772.
Above Left: *Garrick*
Above Right: *Shakespeare*
Left: *Patera, part of decoration above right hand entrance.*

7.2 Other Building Materials - Glazed Brick

Glazed bricks, are produced by applying salt glaze to the brick during firing or, by the application of slip to an already fired brick (usually one face and one end are glazed) and then refiring in the manner of pottery manufacture. These bricks should not be confused with vitrified brick (usually one end only), which have been placed in the kiln so as to receive maximum heat in order to vitrify the clay. Although it is known that a number of the Tamar Valley brickworks produced glazed brick, with one possible exception [11], none was produced elsewhere in the County. Although we have noted during our study that glazed bricks found after the demolition of old buildings, usually come from Candy & Co., Newton Abbot, Devon, it is difficult to be certain of the sources of other occurrences.

Throughout Cornwall there are a number of buildings to be found which incorporate glazed bricks, either internally or externally. Generally glazed brick is used in situations where easy cleaning and/or light reflecting qualities are important. Examples of their

Residential accommodation above shops faced in white glazed brick with alternating glazed green and dark brown bricks as a dressing on the quoins. 84-86, Market Jew Street, Penzance. Designed by N. C. Wheat Jr., 1902. These are probably imported slip glazed bricks.

Disused gentleman's toilet, Wilkes Walk, Truro, now converted into an office.
Top Left: *View of entrance before the conversion showing the brown glazed brick interior.* Top Right: *Entrance after conversion.* Bottom Left: *View of back of toilet showing the supports over the river.* Bottom Right: *Detail of the brickwork.*
The external bricks have a semi-glazed finish which is a characteristic of bricks made by Candy & Co., Newton Abbot, Devon, originally the Great Western Potteries Brick Tile and Clay Works in 1870.

use externally include Venning's Fountain, Launceston Road, Callington, and above H. Samuel's jewellery store on the west corner of the Boscawen Street and Cathedral Lane, Truro. This narrow entrance is typical of the situation where the light reflective quality of the brick is important, so that here, white glazed brick was used to face the upper storey. Their use on the outside of a building in Market Jew Street, Penzance, seems to have been solely for their decorative effect, contrasting the glazed white facing with green and brown coloured brick in the quoins.

The former gentleman's toilet in Wilkes Lane, Truro is lined with brown glazed bricks with a single horizontal row of white, twelve courses up from the floor. This was a typical internal use, where ease of cleaning was an important factor. The building has now been converted for office use and the interior dry lined, so that the glazed brick cannot be seen.

Roof Materials

Although Delabole slate is the favoured roofing material in Cornwall, some buildings can be found with pan tile roofs. These pan tiles were probably imported by sea from Bridgwater in Somerset, from where they were shipped along with other roofing materials such as ridge tiles and finials. Ridge tiles, finials, chimney pots and other items were also made locally, as for example by Lake's Pottery, Truro. We

Red terracotta building products produced at Lake's Pottery, Truro.
Finials: *Wheal Martyn China Clay Museum.*
Chimney Pot: *St. Ives Museum.*

also know that chimney pots were manufactured at the Red Post brickworks on the Bude Canal.

Although we cannot be certain it, is probable that the majority of red roofing materials seen on buildings in the County were imported from Somerset. Cream or pink chimney pots on the other hand, were largely manufactured by Candy & Co., Newton Abbot, Devon. As these building materials are rarely marked and cannot readily be examined, it is difficult to know their origin. However a couple of examples have been recorded. A pan tile from the roof of the now collapsed pan kiln at Baker's Clay works (Georgia, Nancledra near Penzance), is marked "Browne & Co. Bridgwater", while a ridge tile examined during repairs to the vestry roof at Phillack Parish Church was marked "Colthurst & Symons Bridgwater".

A popular late Victorian or Edwardian design of decorative roof finial is the dragon, several of which can be seen in the county, as for example in St. Austell (Cromwell Road), Redruth (Trewirgie Road), Newquay (The Harbour Hotel, North Quay Hill).

Terracotta finials. The four cross designs are from Gwinear Parish Church and date to the 19th century restoration.
Top Left: *Lych Gate*
Top Centre: *North aisle*
Top right: *South aisle*
Left: *Porch*

In St. Ives the St. Eia Hotel has an elephant finial on the gable nearest the road. It seems likely from the shape of the dragons at the localities mentioned, that they were made by J. C. Edwards, Ruabon [12]. Terracotta finials in the form of the cross also occur on many Cornish parish churches (probably resulting from the Victorian refurbishment), as well as on other late 19th century religious buildings. Although several different patterns can be found, we have no idea of their manufacturer.

Brick Coping and Keystones

Some Cornish brickworks manufactured copings for use in capping brick walls. Notably the Lizard Brick and Tile Works who produced ornate copings, examples of which can be seen on the garden wall around what was the brickworks manager's house, at Cross Common, Lizard. Another works was Burthy and examples of their rather plain copings can be seen on some walls of the St. Enoder Parish Church graveyard.

Wheal Remfry works also supplied decorative keystones and a documented example is in the collection at Wheal Martyn China Clay Museum. This appears to be very similar to a pattern made by Candy & Co., Devon, indeed it may be a copy. Other examples such as that photographed in St. Austell showing a leaf pattern, are also probably made by Candy & Co., Newton Abbot, Devon (see p.142, over). From the foregoing we obviously are in some difficulty in identifying the manufacturer of such decorative items, although it can be stated that Candy products which are usually cream coloured, weathering to a creamy-grey (including bricks) and have a much finer texture and a smooth matt finish, when compared to Cornish examples. Items such as skewbacks, moulded bricks for decorative string courses and air bricks can also be found and examples are illustrated on p.142 and p.143.

Brick Paving

Two Cornish brick works, St. Day and Chytane advertised brick paviours for stable and paving use. These have a pattern impressed on one bed face only, which is designed to produce a non slip surface for animal or pedestrian traffic. These paviours, laid in stretcher bond with a patterned bed face uppermost, are the same size as standard bricks. An example of the paviours made at Chytane Brickworks is illustrated (p.144, top). No examples of the use of Cornish made paviours has been found.

In a number of Cornish towns cream coloured paviours exhibiting either a square, or diamond, or star pattern can be found. Examples from Truro and Wadebridge are figured (p.144, bottom), other examples can be found in Caharrack (outside the Methodist Church), Penzance (Lanoweth Road - there are plans to replace these for safety reasons), Redruth (West End) and St. Ives (Fore Street), among others. These particular patterned bricks were made by either Hexter, Humpherson & Co. or Candy & Co. as they appear in both

Examples of decorative keystones. Top Left: *St. Nicholas Street, Bodmin*
Top Right: *Collection at Wheal Martyn China clay museum. Note that
these patterns are similar although that from Bodmin is crisp and more
detailed. It is thought that this was made by Candy & Co., Newton Abbot,
Devon while the Wheal Martyn example (from Wheal Remfry)
is flatter with slight differences in the moulding of the leaves.*
Bottom: *Decorated keystone and skewback, Pondhu Road, St. Austell.
It is likely that both of these as well as the bricks used in the arch were
made by Candy & Co., Newton Abbot, Devon. Note the decorative skewbacks
at either end of the arch above the window.*

Miscellaneous baked clay building products.
Top Row: *Terracotta detailing. Probably manufactured by Candy & Co., Newton Abbot, Devon*
Left: *Pattern used as a decorative string course.*
Right: *Terracotta air vent. Both on brick built house, Leys Lane, Marazion*
Bottom Row: *Tiling*
Left: *Outside pathway paved with 6 inch quarry tiles. Ferris Town, Truro.*
Right: *Polychrome encaustic tiles of various sizes, forming a decorative floor in a conservatory, probably made by Minton Hollins & Co. Blue Haze, The Parade, Truro. Photograph by kind permission of the owners.*

Chytane brick paviour, Wheal Martyn China Clay Museum.

Examples of common paving brick patterns found in a number of towns in Cornwall. It is thought that these were made either by Hexter, Humpherson & Co. or Candy & Co. both of Newton Abbot, Devon.
Top: *Boscawen Street, Truro.* Bottom: *Polmorla Road, Wadebridge.*

firms catalogues dating from the early 20th century. The only example known to the authors, which has been lifted (from Lanoweth Road, Penzance), is not marked.

Floor Tiles

Floor tiles were also made in the County and two examples, one from Chytane, the other from Grampound Road were illustrated earlier (Chapter 4). Such tiles are usually 6 inches (15.2 cms.) square although the example from Grampound Road, illustrated is larger. These are often referred to as quarry tiles [13] and can be coloured red, cream or black, although shades of red are more commonly seen. Quarry tiles can be used in both domestic and industrial premises, where a durable floor surface is required (page 143, bottom left).

Three examples of their use in an industrial situation can be seen at Levant Mine, Pendeen. The recently cleaned ground floor of the Count House shows that these tiles were used in the entrance lobby and elsewhere (?kitchen). The entrance lobby to the old stamps engine house has red, cream and black tiles, while red and grey tiles can found on what remains of the floor of the man-engine house. Some loose tiles were seen to have the mark "Peakes", presumably an up-country manufacturer. Small, 6 by 1½ inches (15.2 by 3.8 cms.), red tiles can be seen on the remains of a floor at the National Explosive Company's works at Upton Towans, near Hayle. These had been used to create a diamond shaped pattern on a plain concrete floor, presumably to prevent slipping.

The entrance lobbies and conservatories of many Edwardian domestic and commercial properties, provide examples of the use of small coloured, semi glazed encaustic tiles, often laid in intricate polychrome patterns (page 143, bottom right). It seems likely that most of these tiles were made by Minton, Hollins & Co., Stoke on Trent.

In Medieval times a favourite floor decoration in churches were patterned burnt clay tiles. These tiles were usually red in colour with a light coloured inlaid cream pattern. The design was produced by pressing a wooden pattern into a partially dried clay tile and filling the impression formed with white clay to give a level surface. They were then allowed to dry further before firing. These patterned tiles were imitated by Victorian church restorers copying Medieval originals and were produced using a semi-dry pressing method to form the tile and to impress the pattern. These tiles were never produced in Cornwall, although many examples can be seen in churches throughout the County.

English Medieval tiles are absent in Cornwall (possibly due to the activities of the Victorian restorers), although some late 15th century, coloured Dutch tiles have survived around the edges of the chapel floor at Cotehele House (National Trust). Examples of 17th century embossed floor tiles survive on the floor of the chancel of Launcells Parish Church. These tiles were made in Barnstaple, Devon. Examples of Medieval and Victorian tiles are illustrated (page 146).

Church Floor Tiles.
Top Row: *Medieval Tiles, Haccombe Church, Devon.*
Middle Row: *17th century, Barnstaple Tiles, Launcells Parish Church, Cornwall*
Bottom Row Left: *Victorian Tiles, Breage Parish Church, Cornwall*
Bottom Row Right: *Victorian Encaustic Tiles, Paul Parish Church, Cornwall.*

Some miscellaneous products made by Cornish brick works.

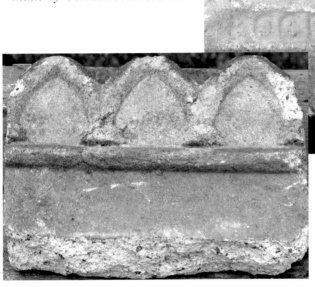

Above & Left:
A garden edging tile made by J. Rogers & Co. (Wheal Remfry).

Right:
Salt glazed chemical ware (part of a tap). Marked 'Tamar Works/ Gunnislake/ Tavistock'
Photo by Cyril Stevens.

Left:
Cream coloured decorative terracotta tile. Made by the Tamar Firebrick & Clay Co. No cream coloured terracotta has been seen on buildings in the County, although it is suspected that many of the now painted tiles on the Toll House in Callington were this colour.

An internal view of the pan kiln preserved at Wheal Martyn China Clay Museum.
Looking along the length of the kiln toward the chimney. Note the brick built flue
walls on which the tiles are laid to form the pan.

7.3 Industrial Applications

Porous Tiles for Pan Kilns

Pan kiln tiles are perhaps the most significant specialist product of Cornish brickworks and are almost unique to Cornwall and south west Devon. The tiles, of a standard
size of 18 inches (45 cms.) by 12 inches (30 cms.), were used to form the pan above the
flues which carried the hot gases needed to dry the clay.

The firebrick built flues ran the length of the kiln and were at 18 inch (45 cms.)
centres so that each tile was supported along each of the short sides. In order to get heat
distribution as even as possible the tiles varied in thickness from 1½ to 5 inches (3.8 to
12.7 cms.), the thickest being used at the firebox end of the pan, decreasing in thickness
toward the chimney end. The example illustrated measures 2½ inches (5.8 cms.) in thickness. Given that a typical pan kiln was perhaps 300 feet long (91.44 metres) and 12 feet
in width (3.7 metres), then the requirement for tiles would be 2,400 for an individual
pan, and, as there may have been as many as 150 pan kilns working in Cornwall at the

Two views of a standard porous pan tile. Collection of Wheal Martyn China Clay Museum.

end of the 19th century, their production represented a major effort on behalf of the brick works which manufactured them. Add to this that they had to be replaced at fairly frequent intervals then we have a major industry producing them. The main brickworks producing pan kiln tiles were; Burthy, Carbis and Wheal Remfry.

Clay dry tiles have had a number of other uses as for example as a building material as can be seen in the doorway of Ruddle Engine House (near St. Austell), where they are used to construct the quoins. They can often be found used as floor or paving tiles as for example at the Hill Westlake brickworks near Greenhill in the Tamar Valley (illustrated Chapter 3, p.54). Here they are used to floor the area between the brick kilns which was used to store the coal and were probably made at this works.

Boiler Seating Bricks

Boiler seating bricks.
Left: *View of boiler seating bricks, in the boiler house at Taylor's Shaft, Pool, Redruth. Measurementsgiving the size are shown.* Above: *St. Day brick mark on the same block.*

Boiler seating bricks were specially manufactured to support the boilers of Cornish Engines and we illustrate one such block made by the St. Day Firebrick and Clay Co. Ltd., showing the principal dimensions (previous page). The composition, texture and general appearance suggests that these seating bricks were made in the same manner as firebrick.

These bricks are commonly found on the sites of mine engine boiler houses and the examples illustrated are from the recently cleared boiler house, adjacent to the engine house at Taylor's Shaft, Pool, Redruth. Evidence suggest that these, like most of the bricks used for the flues and perhaps the chimney, at Robinson's were obtained second hand. Seating bricks were also made by up-country manufacturers and some marked examples can be seen here and at Levant Mine, St. Just; where they can be found near the Green's Economiser building - the large surviving structure with a prominent chimney stack to the east of the remains of the miner's dry.

7.4 Agricultural Uses

The use of burnt clay products other than bricks by farmers in Cornwall, is restricted to a relatively small list of products such as byre tile pipe or land drains, stable (also byre) paviours and drainage gutters as well as ventilators for animal houses.

Tile pipe drains were a common product of brickyards from the late 18th to the 19th century, buried in the ground, they were used to carry water from field to ditch. This assisted in land reclamation and previously wet and unworkable land was drained and brought under the plough. We know from two short contributions by R. M. Phillips [14] that the reclamation of several wet areas of the Lizard Peninsula was undertaken during the 19th century. Around 1850 an initial experiment was made using 1 inch (2.54 cms.) pipes purchased from Bridgwater, to test the viability of the system.

This experiment was so successful that the Lizard Brick & Tileworks was set up at Cross Common to produce tile pipe drains as well as bricks and other products, clay being obtained from Lizard Downs and elsewhere. The works operated from 1851 to 1867 when it closed due to the demands of the Income Tax Commissioners. The tile pipes produced seem to have been 2 inch (5.1 cms.) in diameter and were sold at £1-15-0d (£1.75) per thousand in 1859. Sadly, as no examples have come to light, we do not know how the pipes were made - were they made by wrapping slabs of clay around a mandril (most likely) or were they machine made by extruding the clay through a die?

Stable paviours and drainage gutters appear in the sales literature of several of Cornish brickworks including Chytane and St. Day. The St. Day works advertise stable paviours which are grooved with 4 or 8 panels. An example of a paviour which is preserved at Wheal Martyn China Clay Museum, has already been illustrated (p.144, top).

The ventilation of farm buildings is an important but often neglected aspect of the study of farms. The provision of secondary ventilation in animal houses, other than that provided by windows, is from simple ventilators placed in the walls or the roof of the building. Some examples involving the use of fired clay products are illustrated. The part of the barns illustrated shows two types of simple ventilator, firstly the use of clay drain pipe fixed into the wall and secondly the use of ridge tiles, where ventilation is provided by leaving a gap equivalent to one and one half ridge tiles between two adjacent tiles and bridging this by supporting a double length ridge tile on either end of the tiles forming the gap. This not only allows for ventilation but also provides protection from the weather. The second illustrates the use of mushroom shaped terracotta ventilators placed along the ridge of what was a shippon. These mushroom ventilators are quite common throughout Cornwall and can also be seen on other types of building, as for example at Wendron parish church, where the lych-gate upper room, built in the 17th century, displays two such ventilators.

Farm building ventilators. Left: *The use of mushroom ventilators on the ridge of a shippon. Bucklawren Farm, St. Martin by Looe* Right: *the use of terracotta drain pipe built into the wall and the use of ridge tiles to create ventilation at roof level. The Lizard.*

Terracotta rhubarb forcers. Trelowarren Estate, near Helston.

Horticultural items were also made from terracotta and clay flower pots were an important product of Lake's Pottery, Truro. The photograph at the bottom of the previous page shows a pair of terracotta rhubarb forcers. Sadly these and most other horticultural items were not marked and therefore they cannot be accurately attributed.

7.5 Domestic Terracotta

The principal manufacturer and supplier of domestic terracotta goods was the pottery of W. H. Lake and Son, Chapel Hill, Truro. This firm made a large range of items and as we saw earlier (Chapter 4), they used locally obtained clay as their main raw material. The domestic item for which they were renowned throughout the west country was the cloam oven. This was a beehive shaped terracotta (locally called cloam), oven in which bread was baked in the home.

The cloam oven is essentially a small version of the brick or stone lined ovens often seen built into the side of a hearth in larger establishments such as in the kitchen at Cotehele (National Trust), or in the mess room at Pendennis Castle, Falmouth (English Heritage). Cloam ovens were probably made and used from the 17th century onwards and remained in use in some cottages and farmhouse kitchens until the middle of the 20th century, the last batch being made in Truro in 1935 [15]. The two example illustrated (opposite) are not marked, although as they came from local properties, it is assumed that they were made by Lakes. Of the several cloam ovens examined only one has been marked, that is an oven on display at the Tresillian Barton Farm Museum, near Newquay. This is marked 'E. Fishley' above the door. This example could have been made in Devon as the Fishley family were recorded as operating a pottery in the Barnstaple area during the 19th century.

These beehive shaped ovens were typically 24 inches (60 cms.) wide, 18 inches (45 cms.) high and 30 inches (75 cms.) deep and slope toward the back. The door in the vertical front was sufficiently large, 10 inches (25 cms.) by 12 inches (30 cms.), to allow the housewife access for putting in and taking out, loaves of bread. Each oven had its own door, with either one or two moulded handles (one of the examples shown has one handle), to close off the oven during baking. The top of the oven often has an inscribed pattern of dots usually forming a cross.

The method by which the proven bread loaves were cooked was simple. A fire, using some suitable fuel - often furze (dried gorse), was lit inside the oven and allowed to burn out. The ash was then brushed out of the oven and the bread placed inside the now very hot oven. The door was put in position and luted into place with clay. It was a matter of judgement when the bread was cooked and ready to be taken out. Because of the smoke and ash generated, these ovens, like their larger brick or stone counterparts, were usually built into the side of the fireplace at a convenient working height. More rarely they sat on the hearth.

Cloam ovens used for baking bread in the home.
Top: *Top view of an oven showing a pattern pricked into the clay before firing. Royal Cornwall Museum, River Street, Truro.*
Bottom: *An example on display at the Wayside Museum, Zennor. Note that the single handled door has been placed inside the oven.*

Various items of terracotta for use in the home. Note that some items are partly salt glazed. Top Right: *On display at Wheal Martyn China Clay Museum, St. Austell. The remainder are displayed at the Wayside Museum, Zennor. All the items are believed to have been made by W. H. Lake & Son., Truro.*

A selection of utensils - bowls jugs and containers are illustrated opposite. The large pitcher (Top Left) was used to store train oil, a by product of the pilchard industry. The oil released when the pilchards were pressed was used for lighting, or as a water proofing or preserving agent. The covered container (Middle Right), has a label which suggests that it had been used to preserve fresh eggs in a solution of Isinglass.

A commonly used product of Lake's Pottery was the bussa. This is a large open pan which was used generally to preserve pilchards in the homes of fisher folk. Pilchards, layered with salt, were placed in the bussa and covered with a weighted board. The pressed, salted pilchards were a welcome addition to the family diet when fresh food was hard to come by. The large bowl which is salt glazed internally (Bottom Right) may be a bussa.

7.6 Other Terracotta Products

In the collection of artefacts which were purchased from Lake's Pottery on its closure, by the Trustees of Wheal Martyn China Clay Museum, St. Austell are two other items worth mentioning. The first is a urinal, a bowl shaped container with a drain hole at the base and a flat back with fixing holes. It is salt glazed inside and the outside is plain terracotta. The second item is a decorative terracotta bird feeder partly slip glazed in dark brown. The only opening is that at the back of the food tray, which suggests that introducing bird feed would be a slow process.

Terracotta urinal (left) *and bird feeder* (right) *made by W. H. Lake & Son., Truro.*

End Notes

1 Wedge shaped bricks specially designed for building the top section of chimney stacks for Cornish Engine houses.

2 Terracotta from the Italian meaning baked earth or clay, the term 'architectural terracotta' is used to distinguish it from other unglazed burnt clay products loosely referred to as terracotta e.g. plant pots.

3 Stratton M. 1993 "THE TERRACOTTA REVIVAL" pp. 11-13

4 ibid. p.230 gives a short history of Henry Dennis's firm. Another name under which he traded was The Ruabon Coal & Coke Co. Ltd.

5 Lightbody S. R. 1982 "THE BOOK OF CALLINGTON" p.73

6 ibid. p.107

7 Booker F. 1967 "THE INDUSTRIAL ARCHAEOLOGY OF THE TAMAR VALLEY" p.102 (lower)

8 Huddy, W. H. H. Cornish Times Friday, March 13, 1959

9 Kelly, A. 1990 "MRS COADE'S STONE" 327pp., The Self Publishing Association Ltd., Upton on Severn, Worcs.

10 ibid. pp. 338, 339

11 An important selling point which was used to encourage investors in the Trevarth brickworks near Redruth was a report which stated that the clay to be worked would be suitable for salt glazing and vitrification. As far as is known this property of the clay was never put to the test in practice. Schwartz S. & Parker R. 1998 "LANNER A CORNISH MINING PARISH" Halsgrove, Tiverton. Chapter 6, p.115ff.

12 In July 1992 The British Brick Society published a number of contributions relating to dragon finials (Information 56) in which two manufacturers dragons were illustrated. These were by Barham Bros., Bridgwater and J.C. Edwards, Ruabon and it is from the latter that the Cornish dragons are judged to originate.

13 From the French 'carre', meaning square. Quarry is also the name for small pieces of glass which can be square or diamond shaped and used in leaded lights.

14 Philips R. M. 1963 The Lizard Brick and Pipeworks. The Lizard, Vol. 2 No. 3, pp.16-17 and - ibid. 1965 The Lizard Brick and Pipeworks (further notes). The Lizard, Vol. 3 No. 1, pp.14-15

15 Barley M. W. 1961 "THE ENGLISH FARMHOUSE AND COTTAGE" Routledge, Kegan, Paul Ltd., London. 1987 Paperback Ed. 297pp., p.167-168

CHAPTER 8

NOTABLE USES OF BRICK AND TERRACOTTA IN CORNWALL

This chapter, the first part of which is written in the form of a gazetteer, records examples of some of buildings which demonstrate the range of uses to which bricks and other burnt clay products have been put in Cornwall. There will be duplication as some examples have already appeared earlier in the text and for which chapter and page references are given. The gazetteer brings together the examples previously mentioned, along with others noted during our research. We make no claims that this is in any way comprehensive and no doubt readers will be able to locate many other interesting examples. The illustrations throughout this chapter are referenced by page number (p. # # #), at the begining of each town or section.

Included are domestic, commercial, farming, horticultural and industrial buildings. As already discussed, brick for building was not common in Cornwall until the Georgian Period when a number of large country and town houses were constructed. And, although the use of brick and terracotta in the County reached its zenith in late Victorian and Edwardian times, their use is rare when compared to other parts of England. This is probably due in part to a natural conservatism on part of builders and the abundance of natural building stone and the ease with which it could be obtained. These factors have made a gazetteer like this, a practical proposition.

As brick and terracotta became more generally available because of cheap imports following the development of the railway network and the establishment of local commercial brick works, their use in smaller domestic properties increased significantly. Initially the use of brick was restricted to chimneys and to the quoins of windows and doorways as well as for internal partition walls. Only in late Victorian times did brick and terracotta come into more general use. The use of brick in industrial buildings on the other hand appears to be much more common, although this may be a reflection of the age of the surviving industrial buildings.

The common Cornish roofing material is Delabole Slate, often with red terracotta finials and ridge tiles. There are exceptions and a number pantile roofs have been recorded on agricultural or industrial buildings. One example is Griggs Forge Pottery Lelant, which was built as a blacksmiths shop. Recently constructed properties are mainly clad with concrete tiles which have been made to look like clay.

Falmouth.
Top: *Grove Place, 18th century domestic properties, now used for offices.*
Above: *Detail of the above, showing the use of Flemish Bond with vitrified headers.*
Right: *The King's Pipe. Custom House Quay. Used to burn contraband tobacco.*

Hayle.
Top: *Foundry House, Foundry Square. Granite with red brick dressings.*   Centre: *Faience plaques on old butchers shop, Penpol Terrace.*
Bottom: *Redundant cinema, Fore Street. Elevation of pink terracotta (part painted).*

8.1 Domestic and Commercial Buildings

BODMIN

15 - 19 Honey Street. Stone built with red terracotta dressings, 4 storeys with shops on ground floor, with 3 upper storeys of storage or domestic accommodation. Elevation with 3 pairs of windows each side with terracotta plaques between. Relieving arches over first floor windows enclose semi-circular terracotta plaques. Row of 5 terracotta tiles of 2 patterns below each first and third floor window sills. Illustrated in Chapter7, p.128 & 129. Terracotta, probably manufactured by J. C. Edwards, Ruabon, North Wales [1].

Laninval House, Laninval (off A389, south west of the Bodmin). Built c.1899 of red brick decorated with red terracotta (Chapter 7, p.128), made by Henry Dennis, Hafod Works, Ruabon, North Wales. The architect was Silvanus Trevail [2].

St. Nicholas Street, Masonic Hall. Front elevation in cream glazed terracotta, decorated with some Masonic motifs as well as some Art Nouveau style detailing (illustrated in Chapter 7 p.128). Probably made by Doulton & Co. Early 19th century.

Town End (near junction with Rosevallon Lane). House with projecting bay in cream brick with a row of 5 red terracotta tiles of 2 patterns, between the ground and first floor windows. Set in a surround of moulded bricks, the pattern of the tiles is the same as those below the window sills at Honey Street. Terracotta, probably J. C. Edwards.

CALLINGTON

Launceston Road. Venning's Fountain. Rectangular with base of glazed white brick with an upper course of blue bull nosed headers. Fountain in red Phoenix terracotta (Phoenix Vitrified Paving & Firebrick Works), illustrated in Chapter 7, p.132, along with examples of the patterns used, which include the Tudor rose and stylised daisies.

Spar Supermarket on corner in Liskeard Road. (Built on site of old Guildhall) Red brick of three storeys, with shop on ground floor, domestic accommodation above. Decorated with terracotta tiles in both string courses and panels. These tiles were made at the Phoenix Vitrified Paving & Firebrick Works. Illustrated in Chapter 7, p.133.

Victorian Toll House, Saltash Road. Front and side elevations in brick, decorated with rows of terracotta tiles, now largely obscured by paint. Also tiles in front garden wall of property. There is also an interesting red brick chimney stack with 3 central courses of cream brick. There were a number of loose tiles with the mark of the Tamar Brick & Tile works in the garden. Illustrated in Chapter 7, p. 134.

CAMBORNE

14 - 28 Commercial Street. Brick built elevation, 3 storeys with shops below and domestic accommodation above. Central block with gable is now painted. The two outer blocks are built of cream brick with red brick banding and red window arches. Parapet at roof level is of white brick.

Commercial Street, on corner of Church Lane. Shop with showrooms over, 3 storeys. Top 2 storeys faced in orange/pink terracotta with red terracotta detailing. There is a terracotta balustrade at roof level and a small decorated turret on the corner. Decoration on the terracotta is minimal and relies on the combination of colours for the decorative effect. Built c.1920.

42 - 44 Commercial Street on corner of Commercial Square. Shop with offices over. Orange/pink terracotta. Elevations plain except for round upper storey windows and parapet. Cupola on corner, now painted. Rebuilt in this style by Richard Kinsman after a fire in 1919. Now occupied by the Woolwich Building Society. Marked "RRK 1919" in terracotta.

71 Trelowarren Street. Terracotta elevation, 3 storeys with shop below, now "Main Street Market". Cream terracotta with red terracotta dressings and string courses. Built c.1920.

Tehidy House, 1mile North of Camborne. It is recorded that bricks were burnt on the estate for use in building the internal walls of the house as well as the kitchen garden walls. Because of production problems bricks were brought from London in the following year.

CROWLAS

The Star Inn, north side of A30. Elevation of granite with red brick and plain red terracotta dressings. Gable at east end with red tiles.

FALMOUTH (p. 158)

48 Arwenack Street. Shipping Agents Offices. Three storey Georgian mansion has 2 entrances with porches supported on Doric columns. Red brick in Flemish bond with vitrified headers forming a simple chequered pattern.

Church Street. There are several shops, with 2 floors of domestic accommodation above, with brick elevations, many are painted except Nos. 16 and 17 which, show the original red brick elevation, Flemish bond with simple chequered pattern. Built c.1900.

Launceston.
Left: *23, Westgate St.,*
Red brick with cream/pink
dressings (Flemish bond).
Below: *11, Castle St.,*
Street (Flemish bond).
Built c.1735 .

Lizard, Church Cove. Barn built from blocks of local stone, with red brick dressings and upper storey. Bricks manufactured by the Lizard Brick & Tile Co.

Grove Place. A row of Georgian properties of 3 storeys, built in the 18th century. Now used as office accommodation. Elevation of red brick in Flemish bond, with a simple chequered pattern created by the use of vitrified headers.

Kings Pipe, Custom House Quay. Square chimney structure in 4 tiers, on a granite base. Dark red brick laid in Flemish bond. Used to burn contraband tobacco.

Pendennis Castle. Red brick linings to several bread ovens. It is unlikely that the linings are original as they have probably been replaced several times during the life of the castle.

Swanpool Street. A number of stone built cottages with red brick dressings.

FOWEY

26, Fore Street, Lloyds T.S.B. Bank. 3 storey with accommodation above, in granite with cream terracotta dressings on 1st and 2nd floor elevations.

Town Quay, Working Men's Institute. Red brick, Flemish bond with granite quoins and dressings on 2 storeys. Built 1868, architect Sylvanus Trevail.

GRAMPOUND (near Probus)

Trewithen House. North front of red brick, now rendered. There are 2 detached wings of pink-red brick at right angles to the main house, forming a courtyard at the rear. The house was designed by Thomas Edwards of Greenwich and built c.1715. The bricks were made from local clay and burnt on the estate.

GWEEK

Trelowarren House. Mid 17th century walled gardens of red brick, laid in English Garden Wall bond. The bricks, made on the estate at Gilly Farm, are soft with sandy texture and are weathering badly. Illustrated in Chapter 6, pp.123 & 124.

HAYLE (p. 159)

East Pier, by bridge for road leading to North Quay. Red brick building built to house the swing bridge mechanism in 1877. Flemish bond using perforated bricks. Also nearby, Hayle Gasworks built in 1889. Granite with red brick dressings.

Fore Street, Copperhouse. Redundant cinema built in 1914 by George Bond, which was originally known as "The St. George" and later, "The Palace". Front elevation is in pink terracotta, much of the lower part is now painted and some of the upper part obscured by the addition of an external projection room.

14, Trelissick Road, Bird in Hand Public House. Built c.1860, it was originally built the founders Harvey & Co. as a coach house and stables for the horses used to deliver heavy machinery from their Hayle Foundry to the purchaser. Cream/pink sandy brick in Flemish bond, with granite dressings. It is likely that these were St. Day bricks.

Foundry House, Foundry Square. Late 19th century, built as offices for Harvey & Co. of granite construction with red brick dressings.

The old Cornubia Bakery building next door (close to the Hayle Viaduct), which is mid-19th century in date, is built from sandstone and has similar red brick dressings.

Penpol Terrace, Carnsew Gallery. Originally built c.1910 as butchers shop. Granite elevation decorated with coloured ceramic tiles and faience, showing steers heads in a decorative frame. Along the front of the shop, level with pavement, there is a decorative freeze made from polychrome encaustic tiles of various shapes and sizes.

ILLOGAN

Harris Memorial Hall, Paynters Lane End. Built c.1887 and opened to commemorate Queen Victoria's Golden Jubilee. Sandstone rubble with cream brick dressings around windows and doors with 4 courses of brick on top of walls. Many of the bricks used are moulded specials.

LAUNCESTON (p. 162)

Castle Street. Many elegant brick fronted Georgian houses built in the mid 18th century. Includes Castle Hill House (1730) and Lawrence House (1735), among others. Red brick laid in Flemish bond.

Church Street, opposite junction with High Street. Commercial property with accommodation over. Red brick laid in Flemish bond.

Eagle House, corner of High Street and Western Road. Red terracotta plaques decorating corner bow window set in pink stonework. Maker unknown.

Northgate Street. Launceston & District Liberal Club. Built in 1897. First floor in red brick with stone dressings, second floor clad with red tiles.

Westgate Street (opposite car park). Commercial property of two floors. Red brick with cream/pink brick dressings and banding. Flemish bond.

Marazion, North Street.
Left: *Red brick with flared headers in a diaper pattern, with granite dressing. Elevation of a pair of cottages. Illustrates the use of flared headers.*
Below: *Cream brick with granite dressing. Elevation of a detached house.*

Padstow.
Top Left: *Alms houses, Middle Street. Built 1875 the houses are built in English Cross Bond. The bricks used show some kiss marks.*
Top Right: *Detail of a window arch.*
Right: *19th century mock Tudor style cottage. Lanadwell Street.*

LISKEARD

Greenbank Road - Pound Street Junction. Red terracotta edging to front garden. Running grape vine and grape pattern, probably manufactured at the Tamar works.

Old Road, The row of houses called Hong Kong. Decorative terracotta shield on an outhouse backing onto Old Road with initials of builder underneath a stylised dog. Made at Carkeet Brickworks. Illustrated Chapter 7, p. 135.

LIZARD (p. 163)
Cross Common. There are 2 properties here reputed to be built using brick from the Lizard Brick & Tileworks [3]. These are Brick Cottage and what was the brickworks manager's house. Both are now painted. The garden wall of the managers house is brick with a moulded tile capping. Illustrated in Chapter 5, p.108.

Church Cove. A partly stone built barn nearby has dressings and an upper storey of red brick There are also a number of other minor brick buildings in the general area around Lizard (as for example near Polpeor Cove).

LOSTWITHIEL

Fore Street, Lostwithiel Social Club. Dark red terracotta plaques on side of building. Built 1890. Maker unknown, possibly local.

Restormel Farm Mill built c.1829, of red/brown brick burnt on the farm. Flemish bond. The building has had several uses in its lifetime, the back section is now used as a feed store whilst there are stables on the ground floor in the front. The barn is in need of restoration. Nearby there is a Dutch barn of the same period, with brick built pillars and back wall. Illustrated in Chapter 6 p.120

MARAZION (p. 166)

Fore Street, South side. Row of terrace properties in cream brick with granite dressings. Flemish bond. Possibly Candy (Devon) bricks.

North Street, Gordon House. Double fronted house in cream brick with granite dressings. English garden wall bond. Built c.1900.

North Street. A pair of semi-detached cottages. Bright red brick front elevation in Flemish bond with vitrified headers forming a distinct chequered pattern. Both the quoins and window sills are of granite. The other elevations are of granite rubble. Late 19th century, possibly using locally made bricks from the Acme Brickworks at Newtown on the Marazion Marshes.

The Ferryboat Cafe, Kings Road (plus 2 redundant entrances in **Fore Street** which all belong to the same property). Shop (now a cafe) with conversion of adjacent domestic properties into B & B accommodation. All built as a piece with cream brick and pink decorated terracotta door and window cases and string courses, with granite quoins. Bay above shop entrance all terracotta. King Street elevation granite rubble.

St. Michael's Mount, The Dairy. Gothic revival building based on the Abbots Kitchen at Glastonbury, designed by Piers St. Aubyn [4]. Granite outside. Inside north octagonal dairy partly lined with white glazed brick with a rectangular kitchen on south lined with white St. Day bricks. Raking stretcher bond used throughout. Illustrated on p.10.

MEVAGISSEY (p. 171)

Heligan House and Kitchen Gardens. The Heligan Accounts dated 1692 [5] record that bricks for the house were burnt on the estate and used to build the house. This is now cement rendered and painted white. The extensive walled gardens (part of The Lost Gardens of Heligan), were built in stages between 1710 and 1850. It seems reasonable to assume that the earlier walls at least were built from the same brick used for the house.

NEWQUAY

Edgcumbe Avenue, public gardens beneath the rail viaduct, west side of road. A bench seat entirely constructed out of red/brown bricks, many of which bear the brickmark of the Tolcarne brick works. This seat commemorates and probably marks the site of the old Newquay brickworks. Illustrated in Chapter 4, p. 73).

Headland Road, The Headland Hotel. Designed by Sylvanus Trevail, the hotel was built 1900, in spite of much local protest. The elevations have dressings of bright red terracotta made by Henry Dennis, Ruabon. The walls are rendered and pebble dashed with a grey finish.

PADSTOW (p. 167)

Lanadwell Street. Pair of 19th century mock Tudor cottages red with brick elevations. There is evidence that rendering has recently been removed from the brickwork.

Middle Street, Alms Houses. These red brick dwellings with a central courtyard were built in 1875. English bond with cream/pink brick string courses and detailing over window arches of elevation facing into Middle Street. Many of the bricks show kiss marks and some appear to have weathered badly.

PENZANCE (pp. 170 & 171)

Alexandra Road, Holbein House & Torwood House. This pair of houses now used as hotels were built in 1884, in polychrome brickwork of red and cream on a granite sub-structure. The quoins are in cream brick, while the ground floor is in Flemish bond

Penzance.
An example of polychrome brickwork.
Alexandra Road, Penzance Built 1884.
Above: *Side elevation facing Alexandra Place.*
Left: *Detail by main entrance in Alexandra Road.*

Brick built garden walls.
Top: *Kitchen garden wall, Trelowarren c.1660.*
Middle: *Brick piers outside green-house and brick path. Heligan Garden c.1710.*
Bottom: *Kitchen garden wall showing detail of capping. Trengwainton Garden, c.1820, (Nat. Trust).*

with red headers and cream stretchers with a band of three rows of cream brick. The upper storey is in alternating bands of red and cream brick, each band being three courses thick.

Bread Street at corner of The Arcade. Shop with accommodation over in cream brick with red brick dressings and string courses. Flemish bond.

Causeway Head, shop occupied by Mounts Bay Trading Co. Upper storey built in Flemish bond with cream stretchers and red headers with granite quoins and window with red headers and cream stretchers with one band of three rows cream brick. The upper storey is in alternating bands of red and cream brick, each band being three courses thick.

Chapel Street. There are many shops on the west side of the street which feature first floor domestic accommodation. The elevations of many of the upper storeys of these buildings are in red brick laid in Flemish bond with flared headers giving a chequer board pattern. Some have been painted to emphasize this feature, while others have been painted to disguise this brickwork. It is believed that many of these properties were originally built as terrace houses and converted for shop use by taking out the lower front wall at a later date. The upper storey being supported by a bressumer which itself is supported by cast iron pillars which can still be seen in many of the shops. At the lower end of the street the domestic properties numbers 25 - 27, are built in red Dutch brick (see Chapter 1, p.15), laid in Flemish bond. These houses, including the house which belonged to the Branwell family, can be dated to 1784. It is likely that the other properties in this street discussed above are of the same age.

Green Market. The building now occupied by Threshers was originally built for the Public Benefit Boot Co., to the design of the local architect Oliver Caldwell. The elevations are in red and cream terracotta with granite dressings. There are terracotta shields with the company monogram "PBBC".

Market Jew Street. Numbers 84, 85 & 86, which are shops with accommodation over have a front elevation of white glazed brick, with green and brown glazed brick dressings. They were built in 1902 to the design of the local architect N. C. Wheat [6], illustrated in Chapter 7, p.137.

Morrab Road. The Art and Science Schools of 1880, built to the design of Sylvanus Trevail and located at the top end of the road have a granite front elevation, with red terracotta decoration and labels, illustrated in Chapter 7, pp. 128 & 129. Also in Morrab Road many of the properties have polychrome quarry tiled front paths.

Trengwainton Garden (National Trust). The walled kitchen gardens and raised beds which were built 1820 by Sir Rose Price, are constructed to the dimensions of Noah's Ark [7]. The walls are red brick laid in Flemish bond throughout, with a red terracotta capping. The origin of the bricks is not certain, but it seems likely that they were made on the estate specially for the gardens. A small number of bricks used for repairs have been seen, bearing the mark of the local brick maker William Argal.

PORT ISAAC and nearby fishing villages

The north coast fishing villages of Port Quin, Port Isaac and Port Gaverne were home to important pilchard seines during the 19th century. Many pilchard cellars (or palaces as they are sometimes known), were constructed in the villages in order to process the fish. Part of this process was to press the partly cured fish, in barrels known as hogsheads. To do this the hogsheads, fitted with a special lid called a buckler, were lined against a wall which had slots at an appropriate height and distance apart. To press the fish poles were inserted into the slots passing over the lid of the barrels and a heavy weight hung on the free end.

The principal building material in this area is a soft slate stone which does not weather well. To counteract the wear from the pressing poles, the slots in the cellar walls are built into a brick band of three courses topped with wooden boards which form a lining along the top of the slots. In Port Quin and Port Gaverne, both under the protection of the National Trust, there are a number of cellars which can be visited. The surviving cellar at Port Isaac is used by fishermen as a store. Here the brick used is cream coloured, whereas in all the examples examined in the other two villages bright red coloured brick is used.

REDRUTH (p. 174)

Cross Street, Druids Hall. Built in 1859, several thousands of bricks were supplied by the Lizard Brick & Tile Works. The majority of what remains of the building today, shows that the elevations were of stone with red brick arches above some of the rear windows. Brick has also been used internally, as a lining and for partition walls.

Fore Street, junction with Alma Street. A spectacular example of polychrome brickwork is to be found toward the top of Fore Street. This is the Trounson Building, constructed c.1900 using St. Day bricks with red dressings of Bridgwater brick.

Fore Street, above Lemmin's Court. First floor show rooms with copper clad cupola and dormer attics in roof . The elevation is clad in cream terracotta with some red terracotta decoration. This building does not appear on photographs taken before 1900, so that it must have been constructed post 1900.

47, West End. The old tramway depot for the Camborne-Redruth Tramway of the Urban Electric Supply Co., built in 1902 and used later as an electrical show room. It is a single storey building with a shop-like front, built in Flemish bond out of cream brick which was probably made by Candy & Co., Newton Abbot, Devon. The door, window jambs and sills are constructed using several different kinds of special bricks (see also Chapter 1).

54-58 West End. Shops, with showrooms on the first floor and attics in the gables. The front elevation is of plain red terracotta with decorative swags and wreathes in detailing around the attic windows.

Redruth.
Above: *Tram House, West End.*
Built c.1900, using cream brick with
a slightly glazed surface,
probably made by Candy & Co.,
Newton Abbot, Devon.
General view.
Left: *Detail of a window on the*
Fore Street elevation of the
Trounson Building, Fore Street.
Built with St. Day brick, with
red Bridgwater brick dressings,
c.1900.

St. Martin by Looe, Bucklawren Farm.
Showing slate-stone construction with red brick dressings. This barn is now converted into a restaurant. Photographs by kind permission of the owners, Mr. & Mrs. R. Henley.
Top: *General view of front before conversion.*
Left. *Detail of brick dressing.*
Rear of building.
Brick manufacturer unknown.

ST. AUSTELL

The St. Austell Bank, High Cross Street. Built in 1898 and designed by the architect Sylvanus Trevail the front elevation is in red brick and red terracotta. Above the main entrance there is a semi-circular plaque bearing the date of construction, elsewhere there are decorated shield and other moulded decorations. This terracotta on the front elevation was manufactured by Henry Dennis, Hafod Works, Ruabon works, whereas much of the rear of the building is constructed from local brick from Carloggas, perhaps as an economy measure.

ST. IVES

Academy Place. There are a number of properties here which are built from badly chipped red brick. probably imported Bridgwater brick, which may have been purchased second hand, from the National Explosives Company works at Upton Towans Hayle, when they were demolished in the 1920's.

Back Road West. The detached house named "The Dolls House", near Porthmeor Studios, is built of red perforated brick laid in English bond (bricks examined during building work). No brickmark seen, but they are probably imported Bridgwater brick, which may also have been purchased second hand, from the National Explosives Company.

Fore Street. Knill House, the home of the St. Ives Customs Officer John Knill, built c.1750, is reputed to have been built from Dutch brick brought in as ships ballast. The building is now a shop with accommodation above. As brick can only be seen on the front elevation of the upper storey which has been painted several times, it is not possible to confirm the origin of the brick.

High Street. The floors of the basements under some of the properties here, are of red/brown brick laid in stretcher bond, with the bed face uppermost (no frog to be seen).

Street An Pol. The pair of semi-detached houses known as "Tre Pol Pen" have their front elevations in red brick, with cream brick dressings. Probably Bridgwater and St. Day bricks laid in Flemish bond.

Throughout the town there are many stone built properties with red brick chimneys, red terracotta ridge tiles and finials.

ST. MARTIN BY LOOE (p. 175)

Bucklawren Farm. The farm house and farm buildings built in the mid-18th century are constructed from grey slate stone with red brick dressings. The roofs of Delabole slate with red terracotta ridge tiles and mushroom ventilators (Chapter 7, p.151). Bricks and ridge tiles were examined during building work and were seen to have no makers mark. The bricks have no frog.

TRURO (p. 178)

Station Terrace and Cothele Crescent. Stone built terrace houses with red and white brick dressings. Plans by the architect Alfred E. Harris, dated 1899, specify a dressing of alternating white St. Day and red Bridgwater brick for the window reveals and door quoins. The partition walls were to be constructed from best Grampound Road brick **[8]**. Similarly detailed houses are to be seen in The Crescent and Stratton Terrace.

Back Quay, Lemon Quay. "The Market Inn" built c.1910. The ground floor of the front elevation was in dark green and cream faience, but is now heavily disguised with painted board. There is original red and cream terracotta cladding above, on the first floor.

Boscawen Street/Cathedral Lane. Corner site occupied by Samuel's Jewellers. First floor corner elevation and ornamental chimney faced in white glazed brick with stone dressings. Gable above ornamental wood and stucco. Built in 1906, the architect was Alfred Cornelius **[9]**.

Ferris Town. Many of the houses here have polychrome, quarry tiled front entrance paths. The tiles are frequently red and cream.

The Leats. The building was a meeting hall built c.1860 for the Ancient Order of Foresters and is now used by the Emanuel Full Gospel Church. The elevation is of cream and pink brick with granite quoins, whilst the reveals of the door and windows are in pink brick. Flemish bond throughout and some effort at creating a chequer board pattern has been made using cream stretchers and pink headers. This feature is most noticeable on the gable.

12, 14 New Bridge Street. Shops with accommodation over built in cream brick in Flemish bond. Built c.1900.

Old Bridge Street, Brick House. One of the oldest houses in the City, and is thought to be early 18th century. It was part of a block of several properties which included the Old Bear Inn, most of which were knocked down during the building of the Cathedral. Built of red brick laid in Flemish bond, with granite quoins **[10]**.

Old Bridge Street, "The Barley Sheaf" public house. Built c.1930 with ground floor elevation in dark green glazed brick.

Princes Street, Princes House. Built c.1749 for William Lemon, the house was designed by the architect Thomas Edwards of Greenwich (cf. Trewithen House, earlier). The front elevation is mainly brick, with stone at basement level and stone dressing around the doors and windows **[11]**.

Pydar Street, The Harvey Building. Built c.1890 in red brick with cream brick dressings and quoins.

Truro.
Left & Above: *Old Bridge Street. What is thought to be the oldest brick built house in the City.*
Below: *Station Terrace. Early 20th century houses, built with dressings of cream St. Day and red Bridgwater brick. Detail of door reveals.*

9, Quay Street, The Old Mansion House. Although now rendered, this house was built 1706-1713 by Samuel Enys, using brick brought from London [12].

Quay Street, The Cornwall Farmers Building. Now trading as a wine bar, was designed by Sylvanus Trevail and built c.1895. Elevations in cream brick laid in English bond with two rows of stretchers to one of headers. Red Ruabon, terracotta dressings. The cream bricks have weathered to a pale grey colour, illustrated in Chapter 7, p.131.

River Street. Several buildings with red brick elevations above shops.

St. Mary's Street, S. P. C. K. Bookshop etc. Built c.1900 in cream brick laid in Flemish bond, with red brick dressings.

Wilkes Walk, redundant gents toilet. Constructed in stretcher bond using cream semi-glazed brick with quoins and dressings of brown glazed brick. Inside is brown glazed brick with a single horizontal row of white glazed brick at 3 feet (1 metre) and another at the top of the walls. Externally there are four courses of brown glazed brick at the base with a single row of brown glazed brick at 3 feet (1 metre), and another at the top, to match the white internal rows. The topmost course is of brown glazed Bull-nose brick. This building has now been converted into a commercial property and none of the interior detail can now be seen. Illustrated in Chapter 7, p.138.

8.2 Brickwork in Industrial Building (pp. 181 - 183, 186, 187 & 190)

A short visit to any industrial archaeological site in the County will demonstrate the use of brick in either the construction or decoration of many different types of industrial building. Where high temperature processes were involved, then firebrick would be used, particular examples include the lining of the brick kilns themselves, the lining of the pots of lime kilns and Brunton calciners. Fire bricks were also used extensively in the construction of pan kilns for china clay drying. Their principal use was for the construction of the firebox and flues.

Another type of brick which is commonly found is engineering brick, where strength rather than heat resistance was required. Both firebricks and engineering bricks are standard in both shape and size and only differ from common or building bricks in their physical properties. As we saw earlier (Chapter 2), these properties reflect the composition of the raw material as well as the method and temperature of firing. More rarely, as at the site of the National Explosives Company works on Upton Towans, Hayle; acid resistant bricks were used The best surviving acid bricks are on the floor and lower part of the walls of the Nitric Acid Battery.

Throughout the mining areas of Cornwall, the most significant industrial buildings are the surviving engine houses, built to house the Cornish Engines used in pumping, winding or rock crushing (stamps), for the mines. These are frequently dominated by a circular chimney stack which carried the waste gases and smoke from the fires. These stacks are commonly constructed from granite or other country rock and are topped with a lighter, brick section. The height of these chimneys varies and is dependent on the cylinder size of the engine installed.

The bricks used for this top section of the stack are laid in header bond, using wedge shaped headers with an outer curved header face. These wedge shaped stack bricks are typically 9 inches (24.3 mms.) long and 2½ inches (6.75 mms.) thick. The bricks taper from 4 inches (10.8 mms.) on the outer face, narrowing to 2¼ inches (6.4 mms.) on the inner. Some chimney stacks, such as that at Poldice Arsenic Works, are built using ordinary bricks laid in header bond, which because of the curvature of the chimney gives rise to thick vertical mortar joints on the outer face. Most stacks are plain, or simply banded and with an ornamental top built using brick specials as illustrated. The stack at Wheal Metal near Sithney, is patterned using three different coloured bricks in a diamond pattern, illustrated in Chapter 1, p. 11.

Stack bricks were often imported from Bridgwater in Somerset, although some Cornish firms such as the St. Day Brick & Clay Co., advertised 'stack' bricks in their product list. These bricks were also made by T. Nicholls & Co. at Burthy brickworks near Summercourt. An example of a wedge shaped header from the Wheal Martyn China Clay Museum collection is illustrated on the next page.

This traditional Cornish method of chimney stack construction using header bond is not generally used elsewhere. An example of a chimney built in the classical manner is the surviving 100 foot (30 metres), circular stack at the National Explosives Company works at Upton Towans, Hayle. This is built using a mixture of wedged, curved facers and wedge shaped headers with a curved outer face, in engineering brick. The bond is English Garden Wall bond with 3 rows of stretchers to 1 row of headers. The bricks here are marked 'GWR' and were probably made at Swindon. The stack at Porthia Clay Works near St. Ives, built of red brick on a granite base, also uses English Garden Wall bond. It is thought that these bricks were bought from the National Explosive Company when the works were dismantled in 1921. See p. 182 for illustrations.

The use of brick in engine house construction is normally restricted to the window arches, cylinder and plug doors. A good example is Wheal Edward near Botallack, which shows three courses of red brick in the arch of the plug door. At Giew Engine House near St. Ives, built 1871, the arches of both the cylinder and plug doors are constructed using two rows of cream and two rows of red brick, laid in alternate courses. In both these examples the bricks used are not shaped giving rise to uneven mortar joints.

Associated with most tin mines are dressing floors where the ore was prepared prior to smelting. The first stage involved stamping the ore until it was a fine powder and separating the metal concentrate using a 'buddle' - a system whereby the ore was

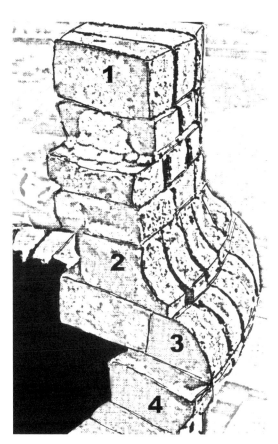

Above Left: *Wedge shaped header made at the Burthy brickworks, specially for use in building chimney stacks for Cornish engine houses.*
Above Right: *Drawing of the top of a Cornish Engine House chimney stack, showing the different brick specials used in its construction. Based on a photograph of the stack at Hawke's Shaft Engine House, Killifreth Mine, Chasewater, before restoration [13].*
1. Wedge shaped headers, used to construct the main part of the stack 2. Concave header 3. Bullnose brick 4. Plinth header

separated using the difference in the specific gravity of the ore and the waste products (mainly finely ground rock). For this the ore was washed into a circular container in which brushes, fixed on rotating arms, swept the resulting slurry allowing the heavier ore material to separate from the remainder. Normally buddles were constructed from wood or stone, with the lining of the floor being made out of the same material. At Botallack some unique, brick floored buddles, have recently been excavated. Here red bricks can be seen showing marked striations, which were made during manufacture and not as a result of wear. This suggests that either the bricks were covered with a wooden lining or that the buddles were never used.

Brick chimney stack building in Cornwall.
Top: *Demonstration of the use of wedge shaped headers as used for the traditional Cornish brick top to a granite chimney. Fallen bricks from the arsenic works chimney, Levant.*
Bottom: *Chimney stack of the nitric acid battery of the National Explosive Co. works at Upton Towans, Hayle, built in English Garden Wall bond using a combination of curved stretchers and wedge shaped headers. Three rows of stretchers to one row of headers.*

Mining brickwork.
Top: *Brick door arch, Wheal Edward, engine house, between Botallack and St. Just.*
Bottom: *Brick built copper precipitating tanks, Levant Mine, Pendeen. Note that although originally rendered the exposed brick work is rotten, due to the acid solutions used.*

After separating the denser ore, arsenic often a major impurity, had to be removed, this was particularly important if tin was the end product . When the concentrate is heated at high temperature in a furnace any arsenic minerals which are present are oxidised and the oxides driven off as a vapour, which could be condensed and the resulting oxides collected and used. Three types of furnace were in general use in Cornwall and Devon, the Shaft Calciner based on the lime kiln, the Flat Bed Calciner, based on the reverberatory furnace and the specially developed Rotary or Brunton Calciner. Of the three types the Brunton Calciner is the most common. All three types of calciner used firebrick some-where in their construction, particularly where extreme temperatures could be detrimental to the structure. They were also a convenient material with which to construct arches for the various openings in the calciner building.

Two Flat Bed Calciners have survived in West Cornwall more or less intact and both are constructed from stone but have some brick in their structure. That at Wheal Coates near St. Agnes is built of slate stone with the window and door openings lined in brick. The furnace, and its associated roasting chamber, and the flues are also brick built. The bricks found here are cream firebrick marked "J. R. & Co.", one of the brickmarks of Wheal Remfry Brick & Tile Works. The other, on Porthmeor dressing floor near Zennor, is built entirely from granite except for the brick lined floor of the roasting chamber. The bricks here are red firebrick marked "COWEN" - the Tyneside manufacturer, mentioned in Chapter 1.

The more commonly found Brunton Calciners, use significant amounts of fire-brick in their structure and seem to have a higher survival rate than any of the others. The outer walls of the building is usually constructed from granite which can be brick lined to protect the stonework from extreme heat. The most important use is for the lin-ing of the roasting chamber or pot itself. Other areas where firebrick is used is for the dressings of the several access openings such as the firebox, ore shoot. Another use is in the power arch, which houses the drive mechanism for the rotating cast iron bed of the calciner, as this is a relatively cool situation ordinary brick is sometimes used. The bank of four Brunton Calciners at Levant Mine near St. Just, provide good examples of these features. Of particular interest on this site is the use of St. Day firebrick linings to the pot and to the several access openings. Many loose bricks found associated with these Calciners are also from the St. Day Brickworks. The Calciner on the landward side of the bank is reckoned to be the oldest of the four (c.1880), here bricks in the power arch, bear the brickmark of the Acme Brick & Tile Co. This brickworks, at Newtown, Marazion, was probably the nearest brickworks to Levant Mine which was operational at this time.

Associated with all Brunton calciners on mine dressing floors are 'arsenic laby-rinths'. These are series of interconnected passages laid out like a labyrinth through which the hot gases from the calciner passed, allowing them to cool and deposit oxides of arsenic on the walls of the passages, from where they could be collected. Although labyrinths are usually constructed of stone as for example at Botallack near St. Just, some were partly built with brick, or were repaired with brick. As several phases of repair can take place, there can be an abundance of bricks from different sources. For example at the site of the labyrinth at Levant near Pendeen (now covered with rock debris for safety reasons) the following Cornish bricks were to be seen: "ACME", "W.A","St Day", "JR&Co". Bricks by othermanufacturers included "CANDY" and "HEXTER HUMPHERSON", both of Newton Abbot, Devon; as well as "COWEN" a Tyneside firebrick manufacturer mentioned earlier. Similar miscellaneous collections of brick have been noted on the site of arsenic works elsewhere as for example at Poldice Arsenic Works near St. Day at Roseworthy near Hayle and at Tolgus near Redruth. Both of these works used material supplied by the mines either in the form of ore or impure products of their calciners, to be refined to produce compounds of arsenic used in the 19th century chemical industry.

When the ore had been roasted to remove the arsenic the next 'contaminant' which had to be removed was copper. This was carried out in tanks placed near the calciners, which were built from brick and lined with cement and bitumen. As the copper was present in the output from the Calciners as the oxide, it had to be extracted using dilute sulphuric acid. The consequence of this is that in spite of the lining, the non acid proof brickwork of the tanks has rotted, leaving very soft disintegrating bricks which weather rapidly in the climate of Cornwall. Examples of copper extraction tanks can be seen at both Levant and at Geevor Mine, Pendeen.

Lime kilns, used for the production of quicklime for both the building trade and for agriculture, are another structure which uses a firebrick to protect the stonework of the main structure. The pot in which the lime is burned is generally lined with at least one course of firebrick as can be seen in the lime kiln on Breageside Wharf at Porthleven, where the bricks are laid in header bond. Many other similar examples are known and the interested reader is referred to Ken Isham's book on the Cornish lime burning industry.

Most of the buildings of the china clay industry used some brick. Good examples of their use can be seen in the buildings of the Wheal Martyn China Clay Museum, situated between St. Austell and Carthew in the Trethowel Valley, where major parts of two important 19th century clay works are preserved and open to the public. These are Wheal Martyn and Gomm Works which date from c.1820 and 1878 respectively.

The museum shop and cafe are housed in what remains of the tanks, clay dry and linhay of the Gomm Works. These two buildings, their associated chimney, coal shed and fireplaces are constructed from traditional granite, with cream coloured firebrick used as a dressing and for the construction of the fireplaces and for the top of the circular chimney stack. In Wheal Martyn itself the clay dry is significant. The fireplace can be examined and it can be seen that its original iron doors survived and when open reveal the firebrick lined firebox. Inside the clay dry the porous tiled floor has been partially lifted exposing the brick flue walls down which the hot gases which dried the clay passed. Also illustrated in Chapter 7, p. 148.

In West Cornwall there are a number of smaller clay works which can be examined. The Leswidden works straddle the A3071 St. Just/Penzance road with the clay pit on the south side of the road and three clay works nearby. The clay works on the north side of the road, are largely constructed from mass concrete. The

Arsenic calciners.
Top: *Brick lining of the power arch*
of a calciner at Pendeen Mine c.1910.
Middle Left: *Power arch of the calciner,*
Botallack Mine. Firebricks here are
marked "St. Day".
Middle Right: *"Carbis" firebrick in one*
of the calciners at Wheal Kitty, St. Agnes.
Right: *Firing arch in a flat bed arsenic*
calciner, Wheal Coates, St. Agnes. These bricks are marked "Rogers & Co.".

Clay drying.
Top: *Flues under clay drying floor, Leswidden clay works on the east side of the A3071 near St. Just. Some of the porous tiles which make up the floor of the dry are still in place. Built c.1920.* Bottom: *Clay dry firebox. Balleswidden clay works on the road from Nancherrow to Sancreed. The firebricks are marked "Rogers & Co." at both sites.*

fireplace end of the clay dry of this works is immediately adjacent to the road and the fireplace arch, the fire box and the flues leading under the floor of the dry are all exposed. Constructed c.1920 the fireplace is built in English bond, with a three course relieving arch above the firing holes.

To the south, on the north side of the Nancherrow/Sancreed road is another works which has a traditional stone-built clay dry, linhay and associated settling tanks. These may date from the original working in this area, known as Balleswidden. The fireplace, is housed in a granite rubble building with well cut quoins and lintels. Inside, the fireplace is constructed of firebrick laid in header bond with two firing positions. The firebricks both here and elsewhere in the Leswidden complex bear the mark of Rogers & Co. Wheal Remfry. Some bricks by Candy of Newton Abbot have also been seen on this site.

Near St. Ives, just to the west of the B3311 St. Ives/Penzance road, near Plenderleath is Porthia Clay Works. This 1920's clay works is more than usually interesting because second hand bricks were used extensively in its construction. The occurrence of firebricks marked "GARNKIRK" as well as large numbers of acid proof bricks bearing the same makers mark as those found at the National Explosive Cos. works at Upton Towans, has led to the suggestion that the bricks used here came from National Explosive Cos. works after they were demolished c.1921. As mentioned earlier it is thought that the surviving chimney stack here was also built from second hand brick, from the same source.

After World War 1 the National Explosives Co. works at Upton Towans, near Hayle became redundant and the works closed. Demolition started soon after and the cleaned-up bricks sold to local building contractors and there are a number of examples of their use, some of which are mentioned.

Two structures remain today which are of interest. Firstly there are the remains of the nitric acid plant and its associated chimney stack. Built c.1890, this part of the works could not be recycled as the brickwork had been contaminated by acid and was therefore not demolished. Several different types of brick have been found here, the walls are largely built of red perforated brick, probably from Bridgwater. Some parts of the surviving walls show evidence of having been rebuilt and a number of bricks marked "CORNWALL" (Grampound Road), have been found here. Internally there are three courses of acid proof bricks at the base of the walls, with acid proof bullnose brick being used to form the window sills.

Part of the brick, acid proof floor has survived and the bricks here are dark blue in colour, some of which are marked. Two makers marks can be seen: "Obsidianite Regd. Acid Proof" and "C. Davison & Co's "ADAMANTINE". Nearby a number "GARNKIRK" firebrick lined flues are also visible, adjacent to the wall nearest the chimney stack. The acid plant chimney stack, is built in blue engineering brick marked "GWR" (illustrated on p. 182).

In 1914 the works were connected to the G.W.R main London to Penzance railway line, by a single track spur. In order to cross Loggans Stream a bridge with brick abutments was built. One of these abutments has survived in a private garden in Brookway, Hayle. The bricks used are orange/ red coloured engineering brick which are unmarked.

GENERAL CONCLUSIONS

It can be seen that in Cornwall there were more brickworks than is generally realised with over 70 sites where bricks were fired, albeit with very varied scales of operation. The making of some terracotta at brickworks in the Tamar Valley has also been covered, and other fired clay production such as crucible making and earthenware manufacture are noted.

In many other counties brick making is largely based on particular deposits of brick earth which are found in quantity. In Cornwall where metal mining had led to a risk taking approach to mineral working, a variety of easily obtained materials were used for brick making, especially in days when transportation was difficult and expensive. It can also be seen that mining knowledge was used to drive tunnels which linked some brick earth operations with brick making and firing operations.

A complication often found is confusion between the names of companies who owned local brickworks and the site names which appear on maps. To an extent this reflects the difficulties, economic and technical, which attended brick making in Cornwall resulting in frequent changes in ownership.

It is likely that other brick making sites will come to light as a result of the publication of this book and will add to the knowledge of Cornish industrial history. The authors would appreciate any information on other possible works.

The manufacture of architectural terracotta has been carried out at very few sites and it is difficult to identify their products readily. Even in towns close to the works identified there is surprisingly little to be seen. This leads to the conclusion that either not much was produced or that which was, was exported from Cornwall. Further research is needed in this area.

The use of brick and terracotta in domestic and commercial buildings is relatively uncommon in the County and although we have given an introduction to the subject more work could be done particularly to identify the manufacturers whose products were used. The use of brick in industrial buildings is relatively more common although the appearance of the ubiquitous perforated red brick from Bridgwater, particularly in the west of the County sometimes gives the impression that little else was used. This is far from the truth and it is from the disused and often crumbling industrial buildings that we get the greatest insight to the use of Cornish brick.

National Explosives Co. Upton Towans, near Hayle.
Above: *An acid proof brick photographed in situ on the floor of the nitric acid plant.*
Right: *Abutment of a railway bridge over Logans Stream, which carried a line to the works. The abutment is now in a private garden.*
Below: *General view remains of the brick built nitric acid plant looking south west. Note the acid plant chimney stack which was figured earlier (p.182).*

END NOTES

1 We cannot be sure of the source of some of the red terracotta found on some of the buildings examined, but assume that in this case that it was probably made by J. C. Edwards of Ruabon.

2 A letter dated 16th July 1899 from Henry Dennis to Silvanus Trevail, relating to building materials for Laninval House is extant.

3 Phillips R. M. 1963 the Lizard Brick and Pipe works. Journal of the Lizard Field Club, p.17

4 Peter Herring 1993 "St Michael's Mount" A report by the Cornwall Archaeological Unit for the National Trust. p.160

5 CRO T1284/15

6 Peter Laws 1974 "A Review of the Architecture of Penzance" In: Pool P. A. S. "The History of the Town and Borough of Penzance" p.198

7 National Trust, Devon and Cornwall News, Summer 2005

8 "Edwardian Truro" 1994, Editor June Palmer, pp. 27,28

9 "The Boscawen Street Area" 1981, 1988 edition. Editor June Palmer, p.47

10 "Pydar Street and the High Cross Area" 1980. Editor June Palmer, pp.38 - 39

11 "Truro in the 18th Century" 1990. Editor June Palmer, p.41

12 "Princes Street and the Quay Area" 1976. Editor June Palmer, p.9

13 Trevithick Society Newsletter No. 70, 1990, p.14

Carnival float by Wheal Remfry Brick & Tileworks using a Peerless lorry driven by W. J. Osborne in the 1920's. Builders are exhorted to buy from J. Y. Hooper who ran the Cornish Mines Supply Co. at St. Austell.

INDEX OF CORNISH BRICK MAKING COMPANIES AND BRICK MAKING SITES

Entries in **bold** indicate illustrations.

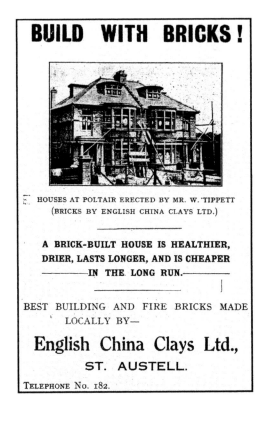

GENERAL INDEX

Entries in **bold** indicate illustrations.

CORNISH SUNBURN FIREPLACES

No. 17.   Design.
18″ Fire, 6′ 6″ Wide, 6′ High.

Price   .   .   . £22 10s. 0d.

Briquettes can be supplied to make this Fireplace,
Price   .   .   . £12 0s. 0d.

Free on rail or lorry, Roche Works.

Another Carbis product manufactured in the 1930's